PAUL DRIVER

Manchester Pieces

PICADOR

First published 1996 by Picador

an imprint of Macmillan Publishers Ltd
25 Eccleston Place, London SW1W 9NF
and Basingstoke

Associated companies throughout the world

ISBN 0 330 34562 1

1 3 5 7 9 8 6 4 2

A CIP catalogue record for this book is available from
the British Library.

Typeset by CentraCet Limited, Cambridge
Printed and bound in Great Britain by
Mackays of Chatham plc, Chatham, Kent

for Andrew Parker

> need I dread from thee
> Harsh judgements if I am so loth to quit
> Those recollected hours that have the charm
> Of visionary things, and lovely forms
> And sweet sensations, that throw back our life
> And make our infancy a visible scene
> On which the sun is shining?
>
> – Wordsworth

I think we should always look back on our past with a sort of tender contempt.

> – Dennis Potter

Contents

Contents

Introductory

Pieces of Manchester, pieces of prose – these writings are an attempt to see the cities of a childhood, Manchester and Salford, from various physical and stylistic perspectives. Like childhood itself they are a kind of essays, in the word's etymological sense: a succession of 'tryings-out'. Thus there is a good deal of overlap between the pieces, which look at much the same thing but from a different angle.

I love the English essay, its compactness, unpredictability, openness of form and to content; but these 'essays' are apt to turn into stories. Certainly, nothing is offered as factual. On the other hand, the sequence of pieces is not to be taken as a narrative progression. It should ideally be revolved like a kaleidoscope. To alter the metaphor: one piece melts into another.

Life, except in its most fatal aspect, is not a linear progression. Disentangling ourselves from the overgrowth on our path through the woods, living by glimpses, we constantly circle round on ourselves, sometimes arriving at clearings to which we know we have had prior access. This is not nostalgia.

Life is the great constant, constantly seen from new vantage points. Change of mental perspective – ultimately the means of moral development – is a habitual process. Just as the repeat of a section in a piece of music always sounds different from before – even though the notes are identical, their context has already changed – so you cannot return along a path without confronting a new world, or step into the same river, be it the Irwell, Irk or Medlock, twice. This is a kind of existentialism.

Those who condemn nostalgia as weak, maudlin, sentimental, and enjoin us to 'live in the present' have a case, no doubt; yet they are also condemning us to superficial consciousness. We all have our reckonings and assignations with the past. *Nostos, algos*: the ache to return home is part of growing up and stays with us to the end. There is more to nostalgia than meets the dewy eye. Examined, it becomes a kind of philosophy, a mysticism, a *presentness*. Not that sentimentality, however scorned, is an emotion without aesthetic interest. Robert Lowell, admiring the 'whimsical, minute, tender, small emotions' of Laforgue's poetry, suggested that 'it's on the verge of being sentimental, and if he hadn't dared to be sentimental he wouldn't have been a poet. I mean, his inspiration was that.'

An English essay ought to be written 'In Praise of Nostalgia'; though the nostalgist as a character-type may well merit a lampooning page from Elias Canetti. *The Nostalgist*: a man at a certain stage of life, riveted to the kitchen sink, upon whose fluted metal surfaces gleams of time are playing.

It isn't only fear of being turned like Lot's wife into a pillar of salt that generates the widespread reluctance to 'look back', but a more generalized and English embarrassment about confronting one's emotions at all. 'Live in the present!' is an injunction to do so with a stiff upper lip. It isn't very virile to savour our feelings, dwell on the past. Life is supposed to be a brisker affair.

Yet nostalgia has a trick of turning up truth, while embarrassment is precisely what one must expect to encounter, living in the present. Nostalgists can, however, lay themselves open to blame for neglecting other people's feelings, if not their own. Complexly charmed by the doings of previous years, they overlook the fact that the doers are more than part of a scintillating human pattern, a body of 'material', but people who may still be alive, hoping to preserve their dignity and secrets. Nostalgists and their kinfolk, writers, make morally free with the past, to the consternation of decent folks who wish to guard their privacy. Writing about people is nearly always, as Joan Didion observed, selling them out. There is an inalienable element of transgression in presenting one's past experiences as a public narrative, in letting the realm of the unspoken speak.

Dishonesty is involved too; or rather a flickering alternation of more or less dubious impulses as one is impelled both to limn the past as more interesting, nobler than it really was – doubtless exemplifying Freud's theory of the 'family romance' – and yet to create such interest as derives from showing it up in all its deadly ordinariness, thereby striving to deliver oneself from, and finally confess to, shall we say 'The Embarrassments of Salford', another conceivable essay title. (What old times were *really* like remains perhaps unsayable.)

But if the attempt to seek out the past can be morally culpable, it may call, conversely, for a principled chastity on the part of the seeker, a personal ascesis, a certain 'emptying-out' of the world of the present. The reward is the attainment of a new sense of imaginative space. For living in the present is always a form of confinement, whether to a room, a relationship, a culture. The world becomes too much with us; we need to surround ourselves with possibility and space; we need to climb a mountain (Coleridge: 'The farther I ascend from animated Nature, from men, and cattle, and the common birds of the woods, and fields, the greater becomes in me the Intensity of the feeling of Life'), or at any rate take a walk in the park. And it is our earliest spaces, our plots of home ground, that are most deeply imbued with a sense of possibility, if only because it was from within these that we first conceived of so much world that lay beyond. Thus they have a unique power to disappoint when actual contact with them is made; but revisiting the streets, gardens, big and bustling fairgrounds of our childhood within the happy confines of a piece of prose – here will be found the truly wide perspectives, best of mountain panoramas!

The workings of memory, then, rather than the objective history of Manchester is the theme of these twenty-two chapters, though the first of them, 'My Manchester', is given over to the latter, albeit in somewhat breathless fashion, taking the form, indeed, of two great gulps of Mersey-grey air.

In a rather existential essay, parks are treated as symbols of (and convenient substitutes for) the space of the past – a living theatre of memory – as well as of literary form. The subtly stressed edifice of memory is collapsed into the simpler notion of inventory in some of the pieces; and the nostalgia question is diversely posed throughout the sequence, for instance in 'Claremont Place', a little invention 'at right angles' to the one of the inventories.

The pieces are of very varying lengths and weights, from the near-epigrammatic scale of 'That Interface', 'Difficulty in Swinton' and 'Two Poems' (both in prose) to the novella size of 'Avatars of Genius', a sort of saddish sonata movement. Musical form is leant on in a number of pieces. 'Ethics and Aesthetics of Grandmother' is cast as a series of twenty-eight (4 x 7) preludes describing a life-arc and mostly ending with a dying fall or fresh act of departure (as grandmothers are always being left). 'Story of a Vowel' is a pocket epic owing a debt to a ten-minute opera for solo soprano, *King Harald's Saga,* by the British composer Judith Weir. 'Involutes' is a literary essay in the form of a brief life of Thomas De Quincey in the form of a prelude and 'dream-fugue' as modelled on the finale to his famous essay *The English*

Mail-Coach. '"Shag"' is a set of variations on the (obscene) word of the title, an 'etymological' and equivocal idyll of a Manchester or Salford childhood. '"Salford Toccata"' in part provides a recapitulation section for the book, touching, however tangentially, on most of the foregoing pieces; recapitulating, too, the book's kaleidoscopic form.

There is little, clearly, that limits what form a 'piece' of prose can take: not even, in the present case, a necessary connection with Manchester, for the subject might equally well be another city or place of origin: the main preoccupation is with consciousness. It does not even follow that the author particularly *likes* the city.

Though, as a matter of fact, he quite does.

ONE

My Manchester

... in the air that is Mersey-grey or humidly tinted by the sun, there hang memories of causes lost or won beyond counting.

– Shell Guide to Britain

It is, indeed, a peaceful night, mild and wet as a night in Manchester, under the massive porch of the Central Library.

– John Ash, 'Three Poems'

Manchester's improving daily

– ballad on the 'Second Town Plan' (1821)

Inasmuch as the names of cities mean anything Manchester is a city built on a breast-like hill Mamucium a Roman breast later Manigeceastre Mamecestre a Norman breast and even eventually Madchester which is more like city built on a tit a city of nightclub obsession pop music ecstasy crack the latest thing for Manchester has been many things though during the Middle Ages it was pretty much nothing marking time nicely with a flourishing trade in wool laying down the seeds of Cottonopolis until the industrial revolution came along and the first modern city in the world was born grew quickly matured declined and well danced but that is to run ahead in the story to begin with there was a garrison at a meeting of roads and eventually the Romans left then for about five hundred years nothing here at all a nice little absence until the medieval township began to develop a mile or so off at the other end of what would become Deansgate where St Mary's parish church lay at the confluence of the Irwell and the eely Irk and near the great dene or gully the hanging ditch over which the Norman baron Robert Grelly built his timber bridge so that timber could be hauled across to make a manor house for him and so it went and the baron won the right to hold an annual fair Acres Fair his son Thomas it was who granted Manchester its first charter in 1301 and a century or so after that the parish church acquired a college of priests housed on a site donated by the lord of the manor Thomas de la Warre in a building which became Chetham's Hospital School and the earliest of free public libraries and after being dissolved and refounded had John Dee Elizabethan magus for warden from 1596 to 1608 by which time Hugh Oldham had established the Manchester Grammar School in 1515 next door to the clergy college yes Manchester was a prosperous little market town with a mill for grinding corn and a mill for fulling cloth and soon exporting woollen and linen cloths via London to Europe but once the weaving of fustian came in that is a cloth with linen warp and cotton weft things began quick-marching to an appointed end not before the elegant St Anne's Square was laid out in 1712 on some of the land used by Acres Fair the city as yet describable as the very image of a radiant garden city the Wythenshawe experiment undreamt of but the preconditions obtained for a big bang it proved a rather short step from honest cottage fustian trade to Cottonopolis all the history books agree for the climate was mild and moist enough to please the plant there lacked incorporation and craft guilds with rules to restrict the sudden expansion of industry and

influx of outsiders and what with the invention of the fly-shuttle
the spinning-jenny the water-frame and mule all admittedly
conceived with wool in mind but promptly turned to cotton
and the tax on pure cotton goods being reduced from sixpence
to threepence a yard the Bridgewater first of canals arriving at
the town in 1762 with cheap coal from Worsley putting paid to
water power and later linking Manchester with the Mersey and
Liverpool by way of prefiguring the ship canal and the first
Boulton and Watt steam engines being installed in a Warrington
cotton mill in 1787 they multiplied all right the industrial
revolution *happened* Manchester became the shock city of the
age a Chicago or LA a boom boom boom town world centre for
distribution and financing as well as manufacture of cotton
produce increasingly the warehouses grew palatial Rothschilds
acquired one in 1799 the Bank of England started its first
provincial branch here in 1826 and as spin-offs so to speak of
the cotton industry arose the engineering metals chemical and
clothing industries it was the wonder city the appalling Coke-
town written of by Dickens also Disraeli Elizabeth Gaskell
Friedrich Engels fatally attractive to immigrants for all the
slumminess of the living conditions never deadlier than in Little
Ireland this was the time of the Two Nations and the population
increasing exponentially the mills likewise ninety-nine of them
by 1830 when the first passenger railway opened between
Manchester and Liverpool engineered by George Stephenson
who had bored the Liverpool tunnel and managed to drain the
Chat Moss swamp between the cities laying down wooden
pilings in parts thought insupportable to traffic the railway
literally floating it was an extraordinarily vital squalid and
socially combustible city feared as the paradigm of social change
and cradle of political revolution the young German factory
manager Engels the recording angel how different maybe for

11

the world if his father had set up the difficult boy in socially more placid Birmingham for a great throbbing and heaving in the national body politic was felt in Manchester there was the nasty episode of Peterloo in August 1819 the Blanketeers and Chartists protesting unavailingly the working man's lot the Anti-Corn Law league under Cobden and Bright's leadership protesting successfully the merchant's thus establishing the Manchester School of economic liberalism *das Manchestertum* but the first Trades Union Congress was convened here in 1868 then to complete the working- and middle-class radical picture along came the Suffragettes Mrs Pankhurst and her girls it was in Manchester essentially that the modern notions of class and class-consciousness were born Manchester being the first self-consciously modern city in the world with the first conurbation the first industrial estate at Trafford Park still the country's largest and all this while the city remained under the legal sway of the Court Leet until as absurdly late as 1846 not a city at all until the Royal Charter of 1853 at which time its ten districts comprised the greatest manufacturing and commercial centre on earth with a population of more than 300,000 soon host to the Art Treasures exhibition Prince Albert's toy at Old Trafford nor had this city of Carlyle's cash nexus neglected the things of sweetness and light there was the Literary and Philosophical Society founded in 1781 the Portico Library in 1806 with subscribers including De Quincey Mrs Gaskell and Robert Peel Peter Mark Roget and Cobden and Bright in a building by Thomas Harrison on the corner of Mosley and Charlotte Streets that is perhaps the earliest instance of classical-revival in the country followed up by Charles Barry's Art Gallery further along Mosley Street and the liberal Manchester Guardian began on its exemplary course in 1821 the liberal Owens College was inaugurated in a Quay Street house in 1851 while the Hallé

Orchestra convened for the purposes of the exhibition has gloriously outlasted it domiciled for decades in Walters's Renaissance-style Free Trade Hall of 1856 a monument dedicated as A.J.P. Taylor remarked engagingly not to a saint or public figure but to a proposition also nearby in the Gentleman's Concert Hall on the site of the future Midland Hotel the chamber concerts were held which Hallé took in hand at one of which the dying Chopin played and the unapplied sciences had been prospering to put it mildly take John Dalton the clock-monitor at the Portico developing his atomic theory of matter bedrock of modern chemistry and his pupil James Prescott Joule a Salford man giving modern physics an eponymous unit of energy and J.J. Thomson discovering the electron and so on and so on and as if to crown it all the great Gothic Town Hall by Alfred Waterhouse in Albert Square went up at a cost of £1,043,838 17s 4d while strides were taken for engineering history when the Manchester Ship Canal thirty-seven miles long opened in 1894 in the depths of the Great Depression true yet vividly manifesting to the world at an illustrious peak of eminence between its fustian origins and formal decline and potently expressive in all its institutions wealth and splendour of the palpable new idea that was Manchester – Manchester

in spite of that twenty-year-long Depression and of the Cotton Famine of the early 1860s the city's economic vitality pulsed on throughout the second half of the nineteenth century yielding impressive statistics unabated till World War I some sixty-five per cent of the world's cotton coming off Lancashire looms for example in 1913 a thousand million yards of cloth sold annually to India all passing out through Manchester the country's fourth port by 1910 with a Stock Exchange trading floor vaunted as the largest room in Europe imperial throne-room of King Cotton indeed and yet and yet world competition in cotton manufacture had been growing apace even abetted by Manchester-made technology while Manchester was failing to modernize its own and restrictive practices tightened their grip there then that enormous Indian market was foregone thanks to World War 1 it seemed the king was slipping by fractions off the throne and so it went by 1929 he'd slumped to the floor ultimately to be democratized out of existence by the development of synthetic fibres putting an end to cotton cloth in the literal sense and spelling doom for mills on mills all right there were the rival industries the engineering chemicals oil and foodstuffs at Trafford Park which eschewing cotton had the Kellogg's cornflake and for a time the Ford Model T while two world wars' demand for munitions kept Metro Vicks doing nicely so that Manchester was cushioned by sheer diversity against industrial decline but after the second war the city's economy must needs be focused on financial and other *services* willingly accept the postindustrial dispensation for the non-textile base was anyhow drifting along the canal to the Runcorn end Trafford Park giving way to Ellesmere Port and Manchester Docks were being marginalized by the rise of containerization and increasing importance of road-freight until they closed down altogether giving way to a spruced-up Salford Quays leisure and business complex leaving Manchester a thoroughly refurbished place now that the terraced slums had long since largely been removed which was a clearance project both delayed and aided by the Manchester Blitz and issuing in a self-defeating sixties' rash of high rises rapidly themselves requiring substantially to be cleared the attractive CIS building always excepted yes a changed place poised for a new century and so on but proud enough of its achievements during this one in the various fields the cultural

scientific sporting spheres your discerning Mancunian in a
certain mood will speak of say the drama thriving at Miss
Horniman's short-lived Gaiety Theatre Lancashire plays of the
1920s like Stanley Houghton's Hindle Wakes or Harold Brig-
house's Hobson's Choice or much later Shelagh Delaney's Taste
of Honey as directed by Joan Littlewood and the work of the
69 Theatre Company which became the Royal Exchange Company whose spaceship-theatre lies suspended above that famous
trading floor which always seems to have been just this minute
vacated by the brokers and he or she will salute perhaps the
actors Albert Finney and Robert Powell and Ben Kingsley
Salford men or the film-directors Mike Leigh Ken Loach and
here or hereabouts it was that musical composition flourished
finely not only in the differing approaches of a John Ireland
William Walton Alan Rawsthorne sons of the perimeter towns
but even in the phenomenon of a new music Manchester School
devoted not like the earlier one to laissez-faire economics but
the stringencies of twelve-tone composition or at any rate a
liberalized though scarcely popular version thereof practised by
Peter Maxwell Davies and Harrison Birtwistle both Lancashire
lads and southerner Alexander Goehr with help from trumpeter
Elgar Howarth an Eccles man at the Royal Manchester College
of Music before it mutated into the Royal Northern College of
Music a conservatory of European standing under Sir John
Manduell's sway these are some of Manchester's successes in
the arts to which may be added a remarkable eloquence of
musical and dramatic criticism as penned by Samuel Langford
George Saintsbury Ernest Newman C.E. Montague Allan
Monkhouse Neville Cardus and James Agate in the Manchester
Guardian under C.P. Scott's sixty-year editorship truly a Manchester unity of odd fellows and in the sciences the achievement
is definitively world-conquering what with the atom isolated by

Dalton being slogged at and split by Ernest Rutherford and a team including Neils Bohr at the Victoria University which had grown from the nucleus as it were of Owens College and developed prestigious traditions in medicine and chemistry Chaim Weizman being a chemistry lecturer there before founding Israel though I'd say parenthetically that for myself Manchester chemistry will always be the smell of a test-tube of copper sulphate from a set bought at Lewis's or was it Paulden's department store as well as theoretical physics and through the connection with Jodrell Bank radio telescope wonder of the Cheshire Plain astrophysics of course then your proud Mancunian will speak of sport for instance Matt Busby's fabulous United teams of the forties fifties and sixties and lions like Charlton Blanchflower Law and Best or Joe Mercer's City stars of the sixties Summerbee Bell and Lee and boxers like Brown and Johnson or the royal succession of Lancashire cricketers the Maclarens Spooners Brearleys Parkins Stathams and stylish sportsmen keep coming forward United footballer Ryan Giggs for example a Swinton man or cricketer Mike Atherton sport indeed is paving a way to the future the city's infrastructure benefiting hugely from bids whether successful or no to host the Olympic and Commonwealth games as witness the streamlined shiny if leaky-roofed new velodrome in the Bradford area and the Manchester Arena behind Victoria Station ah the future the spanking new canal walkways imagine being able to loiter alongside the Rochdale Canal as now you may hard by the new designer bars and the gay village with its fiercely fashionable discothèques catering to a student population derived from at least four universities and the largest in the country a statistic which rather explains the rise of Madchester augured by The Smiths and their lead singer Morrissey and Happy Mondays and epitomized by Factory Records and its

Haçienda club the warehouse home of House music scene of
gangland shootings also the Paradise Factory and The Boardwalk
all ensuring the city's ascendancy in the late eighties as pop
capital of the world yes sparky new versions of Manchester are
being promulgated all the time it is a visually regenerated
postindustrial city railway stations turning into entertainment
centres warehouses metamorphosing into speciality shopping
complexes and brash hotels with Granada Studios and the
Manchester United Museum on Matt Busby Way if not perhaps
the nebulously reconstructed Roman fort at Castlefield all going
to consolidate Manchester's position as sixth favourite desti-
nation for foreign tourists well the man the woman on the street
hardly credits that but the Labour council is well satisifed why
can't the Moss Side problem the crack and gunlaw problem
simply wither away likewise the old beggarwoman slumped
with her trolley of trash by the statues of Albert Square is the
council reprehensibly incurring cash crisis on the head of rate-
capped cash crisis with its penchant for *grands projets* viz the
nearly complete 2,400-seater £42 million concert hall to house
the Hallé the proposed Lowry Centre and opera house on
Salford Quays the stadium envisioned by Norman Foster but
the Metrolink tram network is a boon to all and sundry ditto
the rail link to the important airport third entry-point to the
country now with a height of high tech second terminal for this
is conference-friendly Manchester whither the experts fly to
discuss cities and sustainable development and suchlike topoi it
is service-economy designer Manchester with its plethora of
stockbrokers lawyers media consultants a city to whose centre it
is envisaged all types of people not just consultants lawyers
stockbrokers will soon return to dwell more than a provincial
city it is to be a European if no longer a world one city with a
Brussels tropism novel though that might seem surprising as

17

Michel Butor's Manchester novel Mode d'emploi complete with
street-plan or Vivaldi's Manchester sonatas yes a financial info-
technological and educational city with its distinctive pop and
classical culture and glamorous facilitation of sport its clean-
scrubbed architecture and even a loosening of the old licensing
laws so that the spectre of the Temperance movement may at
last be exorcised on the pleasurable piazzas in the unpolluted
sunshine a place on a breast-like mound decidedly to be hailed
as one of the more glitteringly hopeful of modern cities even if
all right the last place to which such an accolade would be
readily allowed by the woman or man on the street however
pleased with the past (you've got to be joking) is still in sardonic
old Manchester Manchester – Manchester!

TWO

'Shag'

variations on a word

'Shagging' is an ugly word. In Galway they say 'shifting'.

– Jo Brand

1. Obscenity, says Milan Kundera, is the root that attaches us most deeply to our homeland. 'An obscenity pronounced with an accent becomes comical', and our most flagrant swear-words are promptly snuffed out in translation. *Enculer, wichsen, cazzo* sound innocuous enough to an English ear, but never 'f. . .', 'c. . .' or the subject of this sketch. Only they prod us in our English viscera where embarrassment and fear are nourished. Only our mother-tongue, it seems, can give us a really embarrassing lick. Like poetry, obscenity is arbitrary, untranslatable, and profound.

2. I was mooching along the corridor of my primary school when I discovered Freddy lurking in one of the cloakrooms. He was a brownish boy, part tanned, part dirty; lithe, abrupt, a bit slippery, adventuresome. He had recently moved up with his family from the south to dwell in the corner semi at the end of my road. His soft, burred vowels intrigued me. His accent was novelty, privilege, kudos. But something nameless about him

21

repelled me. I didn't know him well and was slightly wary of him.

'D'yer want to meet in Light Oaks Park tonight? I've got something to tell,' he hissed.

'I'm playing out with Robert Byrne,' I assured him.

'I know how to make a baby,' he said.

I frowned. Robert Byrne lived opposite me and went to the Catholic school near Freddy's house.

'All right,' I relented. Where will you be?''

'Meet you at the slide after tea.' 'Tea' in those days was the half-past five main meal of the day. We'd have something like lamb and boiled potatoes and peas, college pudding perhaps, or spotted dick. I would be thinking of something like starting a stamp-collecting club or about that miraculously convincing 'Tardis' control panel that my friend Gareth, weedy but good with his hands, had modelled from egg-boxes and toothpaste caps. I would have just seen *Blue Peter* and be half-watching the next TV programme which would bring 'Children's Hour' to an end. What would that be? *Animal Magic* with Johnny Morris, *Zoo Time* with Desmond Morris, who knows? The news would come on at ten to six.

It was a warm evening in early May. I rushed across the road to call on Robert and drag him with me to this tremulously exciting tryst. I was surprised to find he wasn't particularly interested in learning how babies were made. He'd rather have played as usual in the tarred canvas mock-up (not very convincing) of a spaceship rigged in a slit of ground at the back of his father's tumbledown and carless garage. Dishevelled, bright-eyed behind his spectacles, he followed me nonetheless along our road, past the waste field known as the Allotment, the little Catholic church, the Catholic primary school and round the corner to where the park's pink gateposts gleamed in the weakening sun. We trudged across the great playing-field, for which we'd recently invented the code-name 'argon' (nearly the entire area had now been translated into our private language), and reached the playground, the park's central island, partially walled round and at one end shaded by trees. There was Freddy, scratching about at the foot of the slide. Only a few other kids were present, a couple playing on the ancient creaky swings, a couple on the lumbering spoked roundabout we called the spider's web.

Up we climbed, the three of us, into the miniature roofed house from which you made your whizzing descent on polished metal that grated on bare skin as though you rubbed your finger on a toy balloon. Without a word Freddy unfurled his little penis. We were taken aback, but only for a few seconds. Rubbing two penises together, he explained, was the way you made a baby. He tried to get us to follow his example. Robert flatly refused. I think I may have partly complied. I accepted that Freddy was right in his biological claims, but there seemed remarkably little to them. My embarrassment and excitement were equally muted. A magpie cawed, evening blackbirds were chirping raucously as we slipped in sequence down the slide.

We ambled over to the Gents, a stinking hovel behind the café-house and at the entrance to a secluded yard where the park-keepers kept their rakes and spades and wooden trolleys and made piles of leaves and timber. Unlike the roomy, darkly interesting public lavatory in the other park of our neighbourhood, this one lacked for mystery: a rudimentary open-air urinal on to which stone cubicles abutted whose eye-holed wooden doors would seldom lock. I don't remember much about the occasion save the traumatic moment and its accompanying traumatic word. Robert and I were standing in one cubicle, Freddy was alone in the adjacent. His soft southern voice called out shockingly to us:

'Why don't you two have a shag?'

I wondered if Robert would respond to this suggestion. We fumbled ignorantly, unenthusiastically with our flies. Again it came:

'Go on, have a shag!'

Then an adult voice rang forth:

'What's goin' on in there? Come out!'

We froze.

I appreciated that Freddy's last remark must have been heard by whoever it was. We looked at each other in panic and both certainly felt the need to be quickly as far away as possible from the midst of this incomprehensible and humiliating muddle. The voice repeated its command, and the rickety door took a sharp rap. We crept out and looked up. It was a lone policeman glowering at us in a shining helmet.

'What d'yer think you lads are playin' at?' he boomed.

We said nothing. Freddy remained in his cubicle. Somehow we were hastening along the park-path home, but without Freddy. I don't know what happened to him or how we were released ourselves without trouble. I dreaded our mothers' being told, and perhaps Freddy was in for this. Not that I cared, relief was my overwhelming state. By the time we returned to our houses the pain of the incident had already dwindled into what would be lingering, dull, incommunicable guilt.

3. Deep memory, as Susan Sontag remarks, is more often than not the memory of embarrassment. The lingering guilt we feel about our shameful acts, which latter may be trivial enough, is like a cling-film on the soul. We long to remove this membrane

(like cataracts from an eye), but it grows a true part of us, another kind of skin, the very skin of consciousness. Both the parks that embraced my childhood and seem numinous to me now contained gloomy sites of shame. In the other one, a park of quite different complexion, more rugged and open – whereas the first was cosy, rounded, domesticated – the brown-tiled conveniences bore dank witness to a paltry juvenile depravity of mine which, as it had unrivalled power to enflame me, stored up a proportionate power to shame me. What exactly was it, though, that I did? I can't *exactly* remember. Even close to the time of such intrepidities I often found that I was not entirely sure what I had done. This anxious forgetting was counter-productive, for in supervening states of assertive purity I would torture myself with the minute particulars of guilt, having erased just so much of the questionable scenario as to ensure that I could never know whether I'd done a definite wrong or whether it hadn't happened after all, and I was therefore washed clean of imputation. An episode in the coal shed at our house troubled me greatly in my early years of adolescence when I found the very idea of sexuality mortifying. Months or even years before, another school friend, Stewart, had urged his younger sister to join us one afternoon amongst the glimmering cubic heaps. 'This is the chance!' he had exclaimed. I wasn't in the mood for such a game and think I maintained a lofty indifference to whatever may have been nakedly proposed. But I can't be sure. I wasn't able to say, and still can't, whether or not, albeit briefly – a leap into the dark – I did something dirty.

Daylight flooded Light Oaks Park one Saturday morning when I was playing out with Stewart. Earlier I'd accompanied my father to the garage where his car was being serviced. 'City Garage' had a curving art deco tower and flag-pole visible on a clear day for miles around. Its side-yard and gloom-laden spacious interior were littered with tubes and pipes, stirrups and pumps, tool boxes, hanging coils, a bakelite radio: impedimenta I warmly associated with the greasy friendly presence of the mechanics forever diving under vehicles, and with one of whom, Leonard, flat on his back examining a car's belly, I'd stayed for an inquisitive childish chat while my father did an errand elsewhere on our shopping street, the Height. It was one of those heavenly days that cannot die. After the rainbow glint of the puddles of oil in the garage yard, the shimmer of the sunshine on park trees. Stew and I were trying out various kinds of walking, for instance with the hands clasped tightly behind the back.

'Bet you can't do it like this!' he challenged me, proudly strutting along the gravel path, as an early ice-cream van jangled its tune on what I reckoned must be Saxby Street.

'Course I can! I'm always going along like that!'

He led me into a coppice and suggested that since it was so hot we should risk taking off our trousers. Stewart was a bit reckless and mad, like Freddy, but more extrovert, what adults called a good mixer. It had shocked me one day when I watched him casually stealing from a sweet-shop. I myself had stolen: a pound note from my poor grandmother's dressing-table, and possibly a five-pound note from a widowed great-aunt, though the enormity of the latter crime compelled me to screen it from memory once I'd been found out for the former. Just as I am not certain to this day whether during the episode in the tenebrous old shed I did a dastardly deed or not, so I see before me a silent, cool and lavender-scented bedroom in my aunty's staunch, lace-curtained terraced house and myself in there with temptation. But was there a booty? Was there a crime?

We flopped into a clump of grass, lay stretched and lowered our terylene shorts. We hadn't an interest in lowering our Yfronts, the deed was already sufficiently daring and pleasant. The sun beamed down, we chatted breathlessly over nothing, and after not many minutes I resumed decency, stood up, and bolted home for Saturday lunch, which we knew as dinner. I chose this occasion to blurt out to my parents, with a mouthful of mash, the fact that I'd seen Stewart steal. I took a perplexed gratification from their shocked concern. After leaving the table I played alone in our back garden. I let a tennis ball roll into the foaming kitchen grid.

Stewart shocked me with his language too. I knew that the word 'shit' was improper, but the same word with an appended 'e' left me aghast. (Joyce employs it once or twice, I see, in *Portrait*.) This seemed to me essential obscenity, the unwashed navel of the language. A well-known trade-name for condoms was a favourite shocker in those days, pronounced either with a hard or a soft first syllable, 'dur'. 'Fanny' shocked me less than plain old synonymous 'c. . .', a verbal kick in the balls then much as now. And so on. But 'shag' remains for me the great befuddling compromising shibboleth of obscenity, the very linguistic equivalent of a dark dank deed. And its cognates seem inescapably implicated in its guilt, spreading through them like a stain. The Old English 'sceaga' gives just that 'shaw' or coppice in which a furtive act might be committed, were it only metaphorically sexual, as by the juvescent Wordsworth in 'Nutting':

> Then up I rose,
> And dragged to earth both branch and bough, with crash
> And merciless ravage.

The Old Norse 'skegg' for 'beard', by extension a shaggy mane, transfers readily enough to the pubic area. Whenever at a fairground or a fruiterer's I see a coconut – a rough orb loosely shagged with tapering sisal – I am reminded of the portion of the sexual apparatus that shags, a 'shag' being in one lexicographic submission simply the other portion. To be shagged out has, of course, but one authentic meaning. I let the dictionary's crested cormorant (and long-napped rough cloth) alone. But the 'coarse-cut tobacco' gave me pause when, pursuing one of the enthusiams of my puritanical youth, I noticed that my ascetic hero Sherlock Holmes routinely filled his meerschaum with an act of copulation.

4. The young shag who first revealed to me the primary obscenity of the word, its poetry in a sense, barely himself knew what that meaning was. I saw him less often after the incident of the park. I was always terrified that compromising details might be leaked. I resented what I wouldn't then have been able to phrase as his dangerous silliness. I remained suspicious of his dark-horse character, his dusky sensuality, strong-willedness and independent-mindedness (but I respected him for not joining gangs or getting into fights). I began to find the drawl of his southern vowels sickly. I was pottering in our back garden where my father was trimming the privets one day some summers later when the news came that Freddy had fallen from a railway bridge to his death (adventuring out of bounds as ever). My first thought was not of horror or pity – for his poor parents in their sad house at the far corner of our road – but abrupt relief; the relief expressed in his diary by Yeats on realizing that 'the witness of some foolish word or act of one's own is gone'. But inevitably when I hear or read the eponymous word or someone talks about or tells a shaggy-dog story or speaks of shag tobacco, poor Freddy starts again into life: a vivid, scruffy, intrepid, benighted child; our Peter Pan of the public parks.

Antithetical Uncles

Our Masters' Voices taking our breath,
revelations per minute, winding up in a living
room – turning the tables, taking off – moving: moving
faster (they make us think) than the speed of death.

– Lloyd Schwartz, '78's' (*These People*)

Boxing Day, 1962. As by custom at about four o'clock we, my mother, father, younger sister and I, drive the couple of miles down through darkness towards the docks and into the ward of Weaste, there to continue Christmas festivities, the present-giving at my grandmother's rented house, where two of my uncles, Richard and Jack, also live and Richard's wife, my Aunty Gladys also, Jack being a confirmed bachelor. Another uncle and aunt, at least, will probably be there and their children. Buile Hill Park passes as a curving blur on the left hand side. I shoot an unenvious glance from the backseat of our car into its cold dark emptiness. We turn off Weaste Lane into Liverpool Street, passing the little frosty reservoir, which the road bisects, and sharp right into Church Avenue, whose eponymous St Luke's looms grimly and grimily on its moral mound. The ancient cobbles give us a bumpy ride to the door of the house, which is at the end of the terrace – long ago the family moved there from the next-door house ('It was the Gypsy in us!'

declared one of my uncles) – and comparatively well-lit. Sunlight has, however, not only to penetrate the murk of Salford skies but to contend with a more than man-high, blackened brick wall running alongside the railway forming a narrow and gloomy, mysteriously endless alley.

The house was demolished ten years or so later when it was deemed necessary that a motorway should run through the kitchen, but about two-thirds of the street survives; and if the lost edifice has become a sort of monument of nostalgia sunk into the cortex of my brain, its congeners are still there to remind me precisely what it was we entered that Boxing Day afternoon. Three up, three down with rooms to spare: it was far from the poky terraced street stereotype, stretching back a goodish way before the admittedly truncated backyard was reached; as redoubtably firm-bricked as plain in appearance (not painted a lurid red like numerous neighbouring houses), with a single-storey bay pressing against the threshold. Far from the squalid stereotype too: the exteriors, at least, of most of these houses were maintained with a pride attested by Friday afternoon rubbings of donkey stone on doorstep. Those rough yellow briquettes were exchanged by rag-and-bone men for junk and sold at every corner shop.

Above the numerals of the heavy front door sits the immensely bulbous, shiny door-knob, which it always seems indecorous actually to pull or push: it is there for show. We ring the bell. As we wait for faces to appear in ghostly outline through the nearly opaque glass, I glance down at the few inches of cellar-window that show above the earth of the tiniest of gardens, a few forlorn square inches enclosed by wavy black stone and overborne by neglected privets that is all the view enjoyed by Uncle Dick and Aunty Gladys from within the room they occupy by day. I could never imagine this little plot in sunshine, only dotted by Manchester drizzle and under degrees of darkness, as now. Uncle Dick's shadow wavers on the other side of the door and he opens up.

'Happy Christmas!' he shyly exclaims.

'Happy Christmas!' we answer, and 'Happy Boxing Day!' I with childish pedantry correct.

Uncle Dick is like an attenuated version of my father: the same arched nose, small deep-set blue eyes, curly hair and receding, readily furrowed forehead, but thinner, older, the curls wirier, the build much slighter, the shoulders round, the complexion pale. He is beslippered and becardiganed, neverthe-less wearing a white shirt and punctiliously knotted tie. Smiling quietly, chatting, he leads us along the perpetually dim hallway in which a tallboy moulders and through the middle room, where an alarming Chinese Buddha-lamp sits, down the step by the cellar door into the narrow kitchen where pasty Aunty Gladys in her kitchen coat has been slicing tomatoes and is thickly spreading butter on sliced bread.

Grandma, a stout and radiantly good-humoured lady, smiles to greet us. She is unhurriedly setting the table in the adjoining living room which she shares with Uncle Jack. He's a shabby, shaggy, rough-shaven and genially talkative, very gentle man who always seems to be going out and coming in, a great frequenter of the local picture house, bookies' and rugby ground; unlike Uncle Dick, who rarely leaves the premises. Uncle Jack is absent at this moment but likely to return at any moment. This room is the most familiar in the house to me but none the less intriguing. I love to root in the drawers and cabinet of the thin-legged sideboard, in that biscuit-tin of envelopes with covetable foreign stamps. I always marvel at the size and capacity of the ceiling-high cupboard set into the wall. Its tall and creaky shoe-brown door opens on a minor emporium of household sundries – crockery, cutlery, condiments, brushes and polish, donkey stones, fire-lighters, a perforated cribbage board pricked with match-sticks. It emits a not unpleasant hardware smell which blends with the inoffensive mustiness that pervades the whole house. I marvel, too, at the modest iron foundry of the huge black fireplace, a complex arrangement of grate and apertures and pokeable places, devouring nearly half the width of wall. Long metal drawers pull right out to disclose depths of metal darkness. Coal is stored in a large cavity whose big-hinged doors clang shut. And what a reliable, reassuring blaze is generated! In front of the hearth, obstructing the latch-door on to the backyard and its chilly latrine (the house's only lavatory) bulks a deep-bottomed rocking chair whose air of pre-eminence has survived the decease of its privileged occupant, my grandfather. He would sit for hours there, silently scratching the back of one hand with the fingers of the other, or so I'm told. I have no memory of him at all.

The table to which Grandma is attending is usually, though not today, covered with a felt-backed plastic sheet and strewn with crumbs and clutter: the plastered remains of Uncle Jack's last fry-up, the seasoning bottle dispensing either salt or pepper according to the way you twist the nozzle, the big brown chipped teapot in its grubby cosy, ashtrays, Uncle Jack's racing newspaper or, if it is a Sunday, which is when we most often pay our calls, a copy of the salacious *News of the World* at which I might sneak incredulous glances.

Sunday afternoons at Grandma's, us 'just popping round'! She will be sitting in state at the greasy table. On the primitive black and white TV a pre-war movie, let's say *Grand Hotel* with Greta Garbo, is sure to be flickering and muttering. Passing trains will shrill and Grandma opine in her old lady's squeaky whistle about an issue of the moment, riling my father but entertaining me. On the sideboard wall hangs a gilt-framed oil-painting with silver highlights on the brush-strokes showing a cow at the edge of a pool in what I take to be the Scottish Highlands. It is the most ordinary painting in the world, yet the loneliest image I have ever seen.

I am looking up at it now from the living-room table, transformed by a best cloth of lace, where my sister and cousins Annie and little Joey and myself are having our children's tea. It irritates me that I couldn't have been put at the adult table in the middle room, from which the noise of simultaneous conversations is loudly but not clearly emanating. We have each been given a plate of boiled ham with cold boiled potatoes, crackly lettuce and a giant, juicy but to my mind perfectly dull tomato; plus a dish of trifle. I unscrew the bottle of salad cream and shake a pale yellow blob on the boring lettuce. We say little at our table, though we do manage a thorough itemization of our respective Christmas presents. Annie and Joey live nearer here than we do, on a long declining Seedley terrace in a house which I found bafflingly glum and cramped when taken there once. We soon finish eating, long before *them*. We inspect a cupboard or two to pass the time. We unbolt the cellar door and peer down the cold stone staircase into its dark nether world, and bolt up again. I foolishly suggest slipping out of the back door and weaving through the back alleys to the reservoir, as we've done on summer nights. But Annie just says, 'Shall we go in now?'

They've more or less finished their meal. I sidle up to my mother at the big table and ruefully inform her that I'd love to have a toy saxophone like the one Annie's been given.

'Perhaps for your birthday,' she says.

'Are you goin' to be a musician then?' Uncle Jack grins down at me. 'What about the violin? Be like Jack Benny!' He chuckles with a sharp intake of breath.

'Or *Yehudi*,' puts in Uncle Sidney, Joey and Annie's father, who has small round spectacles and a soft precise voice.

'Anyone want another glass of sherry?' inquires Aunty Gladys, tilting the bottle of Emva Cream in the direction of my father.

'Here, I'll have a glass,' says Aunty Pat.

'Wasn't there a record of his in that pile?' wonders Uncle Sid.

Annie and I help ourselves to Twiglets.

'We've got it somewhere, let's see,' says Uncle Dick, getting up to sort through a black column of '78' discs. On the old Pye Box in a corner 'The Donkey Serenade' is already spinning for the second time this evening:

> There's a song in the air
> But the fair
> Señorita doesn't seem to care
> For the song in the air,
>
> So I'll sing to the mule . . .

'Here it is! I thought so,' he says. 'Yehudi Men-yer-hoo-in. Romance.' He flips the retrieved disc over. 'And this side's Minuet in D.'

I examine the label for myself. His Master's Voice, the faithful hound listening at a gramophone horn. *Romance Based on a Theme by Paganini*, featured in the film *The Magic Bow*, Yehudi Menuhin accompanied by Gerald Moore. We put it on. Oh the sound is beautiful! I stare through the window at the darkened alley not making out, for a minute, any of the chatter in the room.

The donkey theme has evidently led to the seasonal (for us) theme of Newmarket. The table is being cleared of its remaining dishes and a green baize is being rolled on in readiness for our familial game. Uncle Jack, who has had a flutter or two in his time, winks at me and says something of the evils of gambling and giggles again. My mother is talking politely to Aunty Pat, Annie and Joey's mother, who is dangling a fag. She has a rough-chiselled, pallid face but a heart of gold.

'Them's from Fan, too. She sent over all kind o' jewellery, you know, and a what d'yer call it, an incredible kimono. What was Sid's mother goin' to do with that! It's a luvely lookin' thing though.'

'I'd like to see it,' my mother says, looking over at Grandma, who is piping a gleeful remark to Uncle Sid. Everyone's talking at once; and now the record has been changed to Richard Crooks singing a hit song from *Frau Luna*:

> Castles in the air above you
> Ever vanish as you roam.
> Here on earth our hearts do love you,
> Happiness is here at home.

'And, of course, they brought that Buddha thing over long since,' Aunty Pat is continuing.

The Buddha-lamp is truly exotic, a great blue, porcelain, enigmatically smiling godhead, which crashes into the provincial sitting-room with a force of otherness that would quite over-whelm it were it not for the counter-pressure exerted by a no less exotic French mahogany sideboard, minutely embellished, tinted blue, with fluted columns, which has been bought some years back for a song (and will ultimately be sold for a song). It is more an artwork than a household convenience; awkwardly constructed, indeed, for storage, much too big for the room.

The room is really the 'front room', as far as everyday neglect goes. It has that unmistakable air of quiet musty desuetude, doubled in the gilt-framed mirror above the mantelpiece; and that's because Uncle Dick and Aunty Gladys have taken possession of the actual front room. Certainly the bubble of conversation in which we are now enclosed is no less an annual feature than the pulling of a Christmas cracker – which I have just victoriously done with Annie, claiming my rustly outsize party hat and slip of a joke. How do you spell 'hungry horse' in four letters? Answer: *m-t-g-g*.

Newmarket intoxicates us, us kids, at any rate. (Oddly, there is little in the way of alcohol to intoxicate the adults.) We are all accumulating heaps of pence in wins on the imaginary horses and everyone is gaily voluble. Uncle Dick reminds us of the glory days when Great Uncle Victor so far from playing a game with racehorses actually owned them, or at any rate bought them for his employer, the famous cotton magnate and banker Sir Victor Sassoon. This was in Hong Kong where he, Uncle Victor, was nothing less than the secretary of the Jockey Club: an incredible translation for such as ourselves, one who started as no more than a trainee accountant and part-time Manchester pub pianist. This, I know, is cherished family lore, focus of family pride; but I don't remember the details, and as Uncle Dick sketches the outline of the career of his uncle-by-marriage, I am struck afresh by the glamour of it all.

'Aye, he entertained royalty.' Uncle Dick shuffles a pack. 'He once had the Duke of York in his box, the future king!'

'No, that's not right,' Uncle Sid objects. 'Wasn't it the Duke of Gloucester?'

'Oh, maybe so,' continues Uncle Dick. 'And that big house they had in Hong Kong was sold to a film company. They used it for a film with Clark Gable in it and . . . who was it?'

Nobody is quite sure, though Susan Hayward emerges as front runner. No one knows the name of the film either, nor has anyone seen it.

'But he suffered during the war,' Uncle Jack reckons, licking his lips. 'During the Japanese occupation. Yep, that weren't too pretty. Both interned.'

'They may have lost everything,' says my father, scooping up pennies. 'But you know what Fanny said at the end to my mother?' He looks at the latter for confirmation. 'She said . . .'

Uncle Richard interrupts, pointing to his room.

'We've got the photographs and whatnot in there. Why don't I get them?'

'Yes. Why not?'

The game is suspended. I follow Uncle Dick into his abode.

*

Who would have supposed such wildly contrasted destinies?

In one life nothing happening at all. In the other the whole shameful, dazzling century thrashing and glinting and ignominiously floundering. The end of both lives very much as their beginning, but the distance between in one case a straight line, in the other a great tragic arc, a steady though not untroubled ascent to a plateau of high success duly undermined by grave misfortunes before the plunge to the bottom of the pile again. Uncles' lives are not as ours.

Dear Uncle Dick, so mild-mannered yet so talented and obstinate! Uncle Victor must have decided from the start that he had to embrace the world, take risks, become somebody, *live*. I see Dick contented with his fretsawing and homemade toys (2/6d to friends) and Victor punishing the ivories at the White Horse, where he was courting Fanny – one of the publican's daughters like Grandma – knowing exactly where he stood in his accountancy studies, perhaps just another exam hurdle to jump?

Never can a son have ventured less brazenly from the parental door than Uncle Dick, nor seem to have asked for less from the world, nor, when the reckoning is made, have received much less and counted the world's blessings, such as they are, so cheap. He was his father's favourite and grandfather was a man, I understand, whose favouritism meant something. The lack of it bit deeply into his other children. Dick did not abuse or much value his position, I suspect. He merely derived from it an inward assurance that, though he would have to work for a living, he would be able to go through life doing more or less what he liked, making as few concessions as possible, if always remaining gentle and quiet. What he wanted to be free to do was not particularly much: think his thoughts, pursue his researches into holistic medicines, make things with wood, tinker with timepieces. How often in his room hadn't I seen him squinnying through a monocle at an unruly watch mechanism and pronouncing on its condition with the prompt authority of the professional? Behind the lath-curtain of his bureau lay, I knew, an entrancing collection of instruments, spare parts, wireless valves, lenses. And here on the wall was proof of his fretsawing art, a seascape in interlocking boatshapes executed with perfect smoothness, given a crisp professional finish.

The room was, for the child, a bounded world: a cosily dull atmosphere in which Dick and Gladys sat endlessly. On a portable electric ring they cooked their modest meals. They watched their one-channel set, played paper games like Hang-a-Man with my sister and me on the red checked table-cover, and suffered their unbroken succession of ailments. Fear of illness and a congenital cynicism about doctors had drawn Dick to alternative medicine decades before it became fashionable. He rode this hobby-horse with the relentlessness of an Uncle Toby. Everything could be prevented and cured by natural black molasses; or just supposing not, then cider vinegar would serve. He had a caseful of tiny white pills like airgun pellets in tiny bottles: these were his homeopathic remedies, something there for everyone. And it was in this room that I tasted yoghurt for the first time: a daring substance in those days, with a taste that seemed to me worse than that of the sourest milk. My mother was extremely doubtful of the stuff. It was years before she or I started to enjoy it. By then yoghurts had been made sweeter and tastier and lost their raw edge of a moral crusade. But Uncle Dick never lost his.

'Here they are,' he says, plucking a wad of letters and postcards and a cardboard tray of loose dog-eared photographs from one of the bureau's lower drawers. He sorts through them with me, casually flicking through a pair of lives. The irony of the situation escaped me then: the so adventurous career being ultimately grasped and possessed by the diffident relative; the aerial castellan in the hands of the stay-at-home! And Uncle Dick managed to stay at home comprehensively. After leaving school at fourteen he had served an apprenticeship as a pattern-maker, a trade that could have been invented for him; but his fretsawing, patterning skills were soon put to making instruments of war. He was the natural holder of a 'reserved occupation' and held it at a giant factory in Trafford Park. While his brothers were sent across the seas, he endured hostilities in Church Avenue. After the war, and marriage, he had a holiday in Blackpool and another in St Anne's. Never again! When Trafford Park made him redundant not too many years later, he contrived to stay on the dole until he reached retirement age. Thus his working life was compressed into the smallest, most commodious space that his limited circumstances could possibly allow. Eventually he grew tired of mending watches – bad for the eyes, too like the labour he had put behind him. But now he could muse as much as he wanted to and ride his favourite hobby-horse with unimpeded vigour.

'That's a marvellous one of Fan,' says Aunty Pat. 'Doesn't she look dignified, leading in a winner!'

Back on the Newmarket table we pass round the photos which the adults have mostly seen before but I haven't. On the gramophone a dance-band version with glee-club vocals of 'Among my Souvenirs', a song I found so desolate when my father used to croon me to sleep with it.

> There's nothing left for me
> Of days that used to be,
> There's just a memory
> Among my souvenirs.
>
> From letters tied with blue
> A photograph or two . . .

'Just like royalty!' opines Uncle Jack.

'And look at Victor in his white hat here, on a roof!' says Aunty Gladys.

But I'm not very interested in the photographs I'd helped to find and press for the resumption of the game. I do not really examine them for some thirty years and then in a foreign country.

I have, though, seen Uncle Victor in the flesh, or just about. I mean he was on the brink of leaving it, a frail, cadaverous old man, full of shadows, the time I glimpsed him in his first-floor flat in an undistinguished cul-de-sac of Didsbury, where he'd ended up and where Fanny had died a couple of years before. Hale Grandma had been looking after him in his dotage and my father ferried her back and forth when he could and sometimes I went with them.

I see myself waiting in the driving seat of our Anglia while my father dealt with some business up there. The very notion of a 'flat' was a novelty to me – the fat girl in our class at school was the only person I knew who (somewhat disreputably) lived in one; and I was amazed to learn later that in Paris most people lived in apartments and the possession of a whole house and garden there was a luxury. Uncle Victor's apartment was, I'd understood, nothing luxurious – a dingy couple of rooms, a bit of a kitchen: he'd fallen on hard times. Still, I was impressed. This was a quite 'other' way of life. I was in a quite 'other' part of Manchester, I didn't, of course, know where exactly. The little road in which I was waiting – what was taking Daddy so long? – had an atmosphere of difference, even though the houses I was idly surveying in the crescent-shaped stopped end were ordinary enough, drably painted semis with a high occurrence of drab net-curtains. The air coming in through the open car window was moist with recent rain. It was near to dusk on a winter afternoon. A cat scampered along a low garden wall and a train was shunting towards Manchester on the line concealed at the rear of the crescent. I might have been in a foreign city – and it would have been my first.

I had the briefest wander round before Daddy reappeared at Victor's – not Victor's, *someone's* – entrance beckoning me up. So I climbed the short anonymous staircase and followed him in. The cleanly repellent smell of mothballs hit me. I was not to come right into Uncle Victor's room, where he was propped up in the bed that had been specially moved there. He was not well. I merely stood in the doorway and gave a little wave. The curtains were drawn, the room was full of suitcases, statuettes, old newspapers. Lying end-on by the door was an enormous aluminium trunk boldly marked with four initials, reminding me of those of the USSR which I'd seen on stamps. We didn't stay long.

*

Victor had returned to his roots all right. It was from these indifferent South Manchester suburbs that he sallied forth all those years ago. He was, I believe, a gifted boy who overcame adolescent sickliness, passed every exam and managed, though of a reticent nature, to sustain popularity with his peers. By playing the piano in pubs he was scraping just enough income to steer himself through accountancy indentures. It was thus that he attracted the attention of Fanny, doing her stints as barmaid. The White Horse was a tiny place, a glorified front parlour with space for about a dozen closely packed drinkers. It has long since vanished but I like to visualize it as a pub I know in Marylebone: the ceiling covered with patterned wallpaper of a queasy grubby yellow; immemorially colourless curtains ruched along the upper part of the window; a display on a high shelf of dusty plates and Toby jugs; a bronze candelabrum. The incongruity, even, of fluted plaster columns framing the door. The stone floor sprinkled with sawdust. In a tight corner within reaching distance of the chipped, dark-brown counter stands the battered upright at which Victor would settle himself of an evening, trying out each number in brief harmonic outline unnoticed, before tremendously delivering. He had, I guess, a quick ear; could produce the necessary honky-tonk flourishes with ease, and though disliking singalongs was reasonably adept at leading them. An efficient organizer rather than a frustrated artist. He cuts a dashing figure and often wears a cravat. His speech, without being affected, is markedly easier on the ear than the hard-edged, coarse-grained accents that grate unceasingly around him. For all his smooth tones no one calls him a 'posh buhgger'. Fanny's speech is likewise exempt from the harsh influence of immediate circumstances, but she has recently returned from a six-month sojourn in Bristol, where her father's sister, a friend and sometime pupil of Dame Clara Butt, has taught her quite a bit about singing and deportment. She possesses a graceful figure and a genial, almost jolly temperament, sharing the latter if not the former with her sister, my grandmother, who never seems to have envied her, though at times there was absurdly much to envy, and at other times less, of course, than nothing.

Through another, more distant, family connection of Fanny's, on her mother's side, Victor managed to gain a position with E.D. Sassoon, the cotton exporters. He married Fanny. They began their climb. Sassoon's had a branch in Shanghai and Victor was perfectly willing to go east. What was there to stay for in Manchester? They packed their simple bags and travelled, wide-eyed, on the Trans-Siberian railway. He was an immediate success in his new role; his innate diplomacy, social adroitness, kind-heartedness and formidable competence won him advancement and friends. Their son Jackie was born. They pampered him with toys such as my father and his brothers, hearing of them, could only dream of. They ran a substantial establishment with cook and several maids. Next, Victor was offered a transfer to Hong Kong, where Sassoon's had opened an office, and before long he was further promoted to become manager of Sassoon's new bank there. A still grander house, in the fashionable Victoria Peaks district, more domestics, wonderful possessions, high prestige. He became a magistrate. He bought those racehorses on behalf of Sassoon, and climbed the ranks of the Jockey Club at Happy Valley. Fanny kept up appearances, kept them up and up, as if to the manner born.

For me they eternally embody the romance of travel. When I first set foot on New York's Ninth Avenue, it was Victor of whom I thought. That it should have been Ninth and not the glamorous Fifth Avenue that brought him to mind suggests that the mental trigger was the romance of travel (being in Manhattan) qualified by a sense of the seediness of origins (Ninth Avenue as an image of Weaste, of, say, Langworthy Road). Crossing to Liberty Island, I instantly fancied myself in Uncle Victor's shoes on the sun-splashed deck of a ferry to Kowloon: he'd be on a business trip, no doubt, but enamoured of boats as a schoolboy and rejoicing in the great, great freedoms.

For he had got away. (Uncle Richard stayed at home.) When Auden and Isherwood arrived 'from January London' into 'tropical February Hong Kong' in 1938 on their way to write about the Sino-Japanese war, Uncle Victor was installed in the colony. Indeed his employer, the crippled Sir Victor, supported by crutches, was one of the dignitaries they dined with and Uncle Victor conceivably was present. He was in his prime, his heyday. When he returned to England, as on a couple of occasions, it was as a grandee, albeit one being put up in the Seedley district of Salford in the house of Fanny's mother, where he dispensed half-crowns to my father and his brothers who couldn't believe their eyes when permitted to open their squeezed palms. And he and Fanny would soon be off again, to eat up more world. When I finally looked at those photographs of them (how many others have survived?), I was doing a spot of world-eating myself.

I was on holiday in New England before travelling west to visit a long-lost aunt, my father's younger sister, who had early emigrated to California. Making an unplanned return to my hotel room in Stockbridge, Massachusetts, one afternoon when a terrific summer storm had abruptly blackened the sky, and feeling peculiarly disoriented and alone, I plucked out the brown envelope of the photographs from the bottom of my travelling bag and shook them on to the bed. The wind whistled, the window-frames rattled. Under the glaring electric bulb, in the naked contingency of my own life, I beheld the extraordinary triumph over circumstances that was Victor's and Fanny's, for a while.

Here is Fanny leading that winning horse into the ring. Goodness, how regal she really does look! A sunny, summery day, she in rippling dress of polka-dotted silk with white stockings and shoes and crocodile handbag under an arm, both arms bent in a light grasp of the reins and one foot forward, caught as she has been by the camera in an instant of walking, instant of joy. She strides confidently towards – me! Her spontaneous yet dignified smile is overshadowed by her floppy sun hat, as is Victor's face by his trilby as he follows a couple of steps behind her at a statelier pace. He wears a white linen suit like nearly everyone in the sizeable, nearly all-male crowd. His jacket is double-buttoned at the medium-sized belly and slightly rumpled, his right trouser leg blows in the breeze as he walks. He is large and stocky of build, a touch portly, a touch round-shouldered. He sports a bow-tie, dangles a watch between lapel and breast pocket, and seems to be half-smiling in a way that both fits his dignity and betrays his pride in Fanny. His hands at hips are noticeably podgy, venous, with the rough texture of hide, the hands of a doer. Victor and Fanny tread the horse's shadow, printed on the summer turf; and a hatless, bespectacled Chinese man, almost out of the picture, applauds their progress. The limber Chinese jockey, eyes bashfully down, grins hand-somely upon his victorious mount, the damp suede of whose breast one can practically stroke. But many of the bystanders are looking beyond Fanny and Victor at the next incoming winner. The sunlit hills are blurred in the not too distant background. In the clubhouse afternoon cocktails are being served. It is a day in the youth of the world! It is real. This black and white photograph, torn by the use of decades into three strips, stained, yellowed, crinkled, ever fracturing further, is extraordinarily surviving evidence of something so mysteriously and terribly, terribly actual.

And yet it is also the quaintly historical world of those early black and white movies glimmering in my grandmother's living room. This impression I gain the more vividly from another snapshot of Fanny stylishly leading in a horse, taken a few years before in a different season. She is wrapped sinuously in an opulent fur of the 1930s and wears a fashionably rounded hat, bag clasped again under left arm, just one hand on the reins. Several spectators, men and women, are in Chinese dress, deliciously elegant. One Chinese man, in a Western dark suit and spats, clutches a pen and notebook to his leg, and has a stern, quizzical expression as he scrutinizes Fanny. Who is he? The successful jockey has a rather serious sort of smile and resembles Cary Grant. And I, grazing the past, allow them life.

Here is one of Victor and Fanny 'being received by the host at a cocktail party', as she herself has inscribed the back. She is all poise and graciousness, this time in a floral dress discreetly frilled with lace and diamond earrings (as I suspect) glinting: it is a far cry from the White Horse, but perhaps the social skills she developed back then haven't proved entirely irrelevant in this upper echelon. She shakes the hand of the Chinese host who bends forward with a dazzling smile, glass in hand; while Victor, bulking, beaming, clad like their host in pristine white, but a dark tie beneath his studded collar, is glancing across the room, his eyes alight. A scene from *Grand Hotel*! The tanned bare arm of a young woman involved with a smiling young man in black bow-tie immediately behind Fanny contrasts with her own bare arm, thinner, paler. They are older now.

Yes, it is thirty years after this snap marked 'Victor serious Taken on the hotel roof', the most beguiling of these images of him. Semi-recumbent on a bamboo chair, in habitual white suit with dicky bow, pudding-basin white hat, white shoes and spats and a nearly spent cigarette between thumb and two fingers of the upraised left hand, he looks not so much serious as enigmatic, reflective, ironically amused. His face is striking but quite ugly really: the turned-up nose, the awkward chin are more noticeable in his younger self than in the bland face-set, smoothed by the years, of the smiling public man. But by now he is already a public man, I suppose; prosperous, sitting out a few moments in the privacy of the roof garden with its mosquito net and wrought-iron balustrade through which Hong Kong is mistily, grandly outlined. His spats and the rakish angle of his left foot on the asphalt rooftop hold me. He cuts a dashing figure even if the hat is too big for him and the boy still visibly metamorphosing into the man.

In this photograph – who took it? Fanny, I presume – Victor may or may not be taking stock of his life but can be seen as perfectly poised on the fulcrum of his past and future. He would become more prosperous, a good deal more; and he would suffer tragedies. As I sit on the bed in Stockbridge trying to connect these random pieces of two lives – the capricious title of a Wallace Stevens poem, 'Someone Puts a Pineapple Together' pops into my head – I suddenly see *me* staring back at me. It's a photograph of a little boy in a nursery with a little girl playmate holding the strap of a box camera. The boy is Jackie, Victor's and Fanny's only child, smartly turned out in shirt and neckerchief, seated at the pedals of a fancy, patently expensive toy motor-car and grumpily presenting to the camera the selfsame forehead and hairline of myself as a young child. The mouth is appropriately that of his namesake, my Uncle Jack, the cousin whom he never lived to see. He died of hydrophobia at eleven years of age. Victor never ceased to blame the doctors in Shanghai for incompetence nor rebuke himself for not suing them. Absurd. The child's photographic image is ghostlier than that of his parents – he had so little time to make an impact, a comma on the text of the world, before joining the dust of China – but no less real. Here I am, poring over him more than seventy years on, trying to imagine and empathize with the sorrow.

Lesser afflictions for Victor and Fanny were to follow in a spate. I try to sort out the dates of these photographs, slipped from history's slush-pile, three of which are small picture-postcards of the skyscraperless colony and bear a continuous message to my grandmother dated 'Hotel Cecil, April 1947'. The year, then, of Stevens's pineapple; the aftermath of wartime internment for the British residents of Hong Kong. Victor and Fanny had been on holiday in Java when the Japanese invasion took place. Victor was allowed out but on returning to Hong Kong was consigned to Stanley Camp. Fanny was prevented from leaving but eventually escaped to Shanghai, where she stayed with a German lady whom she knew but slightly. She was soon found out by the Japanese and despatched to the Lung War Camp in Hong Kong. Eighteen months passed.

Stanley Camp, in a bay of inlets on the south side of the island, wafted by Mediterranean airs, was, I learn, a 'grotesque microcosm' of Hong Kong's civilian society, a servantless social quagmire in which everyone scrabbled for rank but made his strict obeisances to the Japanese if he wanted to evade summary torture or execution. Victor, in his usual quiet way, quickly became leader of his group of inmates and did what he could to ease their lot. He helped to put on revues, playing the piano himself, a doubtless battered instrument that must have revived poignant memories of Manchester. He successfully negotiated with the Japanese authorities – the British 'authorities' were still, at least in their own estimation, in place within the camp – for clemency to his charges on several occasions. He was, so family lore insists, a bit of a hero.

And both Fanny and he survived their ordeals with their sanity intact, even if they drastically lost weight, fifty per cent of it in Victor's case, and, it's said, walked past each other in a hospital corridor without recognition. They lost, too, most of their possessions. The trusty Chinese housekeeper who had remained in their handsome villa had had to sell anything with the smallest street value in order to eat. My father, uncles and aunts love to speculate about what must have gone. Much of quaintness, if not of value, nevertheless survived, even to adorn my own childhood bedroom. The house itself, which had been bomb-damaged, now had to be sold; it went to MGM. Victor and Fanny lived for a while in a cheapish hotel where she filled the reverse sides of these three touching old views – the first a glittering sweep of city, hills and harbour, the second showing the old Hong Kong and Shanghai Bank and the faint vertical line of the Peak tram, the third an uncharacteristically unbustling Queen's Road – with her strongly flowing, curlicued, blue-inked, unfaded script.

This is the lovely view we get, she writes, from Macdonnell Rd. We used to see all the big ships coming into the harbour. It is awful to see, most of the houses have been bombed and will cost more now, to repair them. One cannot get a house or flat. Not an office to be had, people are offering any amount of money to get one. The place is crowded with Shanghai Chinese, all want to open offices here . . . I tried to get a book of views, but they're not making them

49

yet, owing to the paper shortage . . . We feel so unsettled, we haven't unpacked yet. I hate packing and unpacking . . .

She doesn't properly 'pack' her letter either, each of the cards ends without a full stop. As the rain beat down in Stockbridge I thought of Uncle Richard, who rarely packed or unpacked, who stayed at home.

As for Uncle Victor, another calamity soon befell him. He was shockingly dismissed from his post at Sassoon's bank. It was alleged that he authorized a bad loan against the wishes of his superior at a time when Sir Victor himself was absent. But Uncle Victor vehemently denied wrongdoing and maintained to his Didsbury deathbed, as my father testifies, that he had been framed. He wrote a six-page letter in self-extenuation: Manchester cupboards and drawers have been combed in search of the bruised brown leather pouch in which a copy of the typescript was supposed to be preserved. But Victor's *apologia pro vita sua* may have gone for ever.

His doings over the next decade remain still murkier. Jobless, he sailed with Fanny back to England, but finding nothing for himself there, returned to the Far East and, as the family still loves to recount, nearly made himself a millionaire. He was setting up a munitions factory in Korea and about to clinch a lucrative deal with the Russians, when, with his world-historical bad luck, a war broke on his head and the Americans bombed the place. What the intricacies of loyalty and patriotism were in this episode, I don't know. What kind of a man was Victor? How many betrayals had he on his conscience, if any? I see only a man in a white suit bobbing helplessly on the troubled waters of the century, a man who had lost his only child, his home, his livelihood, his civic standing and all his money. There was nothing for Fanny and Victor to do now but return to England

Antithetical Uncles

for good. Their life together, of which these are but sorry glimpses, described the final segment of its arc.

Munitions factories in Korea! No one could be less like an entrepreneur than Uncle Dick, though, true, he had worked in that sort of factory. *His* life was one of renunciation and dogged privacy. He hadn't been to the east. He hadn't, unlike his younger sister – whom I failed to find in California, so she never got to see the photographs – been to the west. He'd barely touched on Blackpool. So much of life flowed past him. But he had his homeopathic remedies.

*

Grandma was not displeased, of course, to have her sister back, and Fanny was not unduly distraught about her new circumstances. Stout-hearted, she told her sister, 'If I had my time over again, I'd do it all just the same. I've had a wonderful life!' But her health was unmendably broken. She would never have aged into a splendid physical stoutness, as Grandma did, but could not even sustain her proper weight. Worldly experience had thinned her irredeemably, whereas domestic stability, rootedness to the spot, had perfectly solidified Grandma. Fanny just faded away. Then began Grandma's two years of regularly tending Victor. He had not come home with equanimity, he was full of remorse and regrets. He grew gloomier and gruffer and heavily passive, seldom leaving the Didsbury flat, as though to mock his life of action or, at any rate, ensure that Didsbury didn't mock it. He had a few old traveller's yarns to spin for my father but infallibly reverted to Sassoon, and my father was usually glad to get away. Victor developed bronchitis, became bedridden. It was when he was close to expiry that, as my father tells it, he grabbed at Grandma's hand and whispered, 'Fetch

my will out of that bureau, will you.' It had yet to be signed, a
task he was barely strong enough to perform. He had repeatedly
told her that she was the only beneficiary, not that he had much
to leave now. He asked for his sleek gold fountain-pen out of
the bureau drawer and, sitting up in bed with effort, with a
greater effort frailly scratched his name upon the elderly
document.

'Now go and get that witnessed!' he commanded her.

Poor woman, she did not grasp the niceties of these affairs.
She marched into the nearest grocer's and secured his signature
as witness – to nothing! He too might have known better. But
it was essentially Victor, once universally esteemed as a banker
and accountant in Hong Kong, who botched the signing of his
own will. There was, indeed, little left in his estate: about five
hundred pounds, some of Fanny's jewellery and otherwise items
of memorabilia. It was a spinster relation of whom no one had
ever heard who inherited it all. My grandmother could have
used the money; she had little enough to leave in her own will.
But mementoes and even a couple of pieces of jewellery had,
however, passed to my parents before Victor died. Each time
he returned from a visit my father would bring some booty.
That aluminium trunk, which Fanny so disliked packing and
unpacking, its inside reeking of mothballs, found a new desti-
nation in the trim loft of our Salford semi, and doubtless its last.
The gold fountain-pen with its long, strong nib and suction cap
(but I wasn't supposed to play with it), a grey and silver
propelling pencil with a casket of leads secreted inside like a
miniature time-capsule, an assortment of coins and ribboned
Jockey Club medals – all these and more we received, blessed,
pathetic tokens of an otherness, which retain their aura. Oh,
and the diminishing sequence of little ebony elephants with

ivory tusks which dropped off one by one in our cool porch over the years, until there were none.

*

Why is it that one remembers certain scenes of one's childhood for their very boredom, when the state of being bored is precisely what one would have expected the sifting brain to censor? But there I forever am, sitting on a step in the vast necropolis of Southern Cemetery in Didsbury one endless Sunday afternoon, with memory's dear old sun proverbially shining. The flagstones are warm, I have an ice-cream cornet in my sticky hand, and I am waiting. I am waiting for Grandma, dutiful to the dead as to the living, to emerge from the labyrinth of tombs where both Fanny and now Victor are to be found. I am pondering whether we might get away from here in time for me to do something interesting (unlikely) or at least catch *Space Patrol* on the ITV. My father and mother are present, but right now absent. What are they doing? I watch other families passing in and out through the cemetery gates, boys like myself in terylene shorts and light-brown sandals and some unfortunates rigged out in appalling Sunday suits, squirming in the heat (so things could be worse). *Southern Cemetery*, I pronounce to myself. Are there corresponding cemeteries at other points of the compass?

Eventually they all reappear and I am rewarded for my wait with the promise of a sweetshop detour on the way home. Despite that, and for all the loveliness of the sunshine, I take a sense of pure dreariness from the afternoon as we drive along Seymour Grove and over the swing-bridge at White City. It is one of those unfocused, irritable Sundays that bear down on children so heavily. I have to keep readjusting the sit of my underpants in the back of the car; my nose is blocked; I'm peckish as always and vaguely dread the resumption of school next day. There's nothing to look forward to except television, then it will be bedtime in daylight. If something of consequence has happened it hasn't touched the dull equilibrium of my own life. There seems to be no mourning sadness about the death of Uncle Victor filling the vehicle.

The vigorous antithesis to such Sundays is surely Boxing Day, a day safely wedged into the holiday bloc and the season of dark cosy nights and a day for continuing the adventure of presents. Resting now on the baize of the Newmarket table, my mother's venose hand, I notice, is displaying one of Fanny's rings, the beautiful sapphire that Grandma gave her. My father has just re-conveyed that verdict of Fanny's on her life and the testamentary muddle has occasioned a fresh round of rueful remarks and a railway-screech of mock anger from Grandma. On the gramophone Richard Tauber is singing Toselli's *Serenade*, one of the German 78s that Uncle Sidney hauled back from war service along with some classical items, such as Benno Moiseiwitsch in the *Moonlight Sonata*. Uncle Sidney cocks an ear in collector's pride or because he is struck by the extraordinary beauty of the singer's tone. No one else seems to be listening; we are preoccupied with counting our winnings.

'You've broken the bank!' Uncle Jack chuckles at me.

An actual train whistles by, the last one of Boxing Day, so Uncle Jack observes.

'They don't make tenors like Tauber any more,' Uncle Dick abruptly asserts. 'Nor Josef Locke either.'

Is it true? Has that sort of voice become extinct?

I pondered the question years afterward when playing these very discs on a newly acquired Trixette. That incredible legato ease and sadness, that utterly seductive eloquence, with the

inbuilt sob, extinct? Josef Locke pouring forth 'My Heart and I'
(how svelte a vowel they used to use for 'I': *af*!), Tino Rossi in
'Tristesse' (what accomplished heartbreak!), Lawrence Tibbett
singing of 'Myself When Young' . . . Oh I melt! And where are
the great crooners? The Bings, the Perrys – they, too, so
beguilingly smooth, communicating so frankly and generously
across what length of years! I'm fascinated by the little brittle
disc, so vulnerable to time, on the black and gold Brunswick
label, of Perry Como in 'I Wonder Who's Kissing Her Now?'
with Ted Weems and his orchestra. A world floods into the
room, woody clarinets brightly to the fore, guitar thrumming in
the bass, trad jazz trumpets and trombones blaring out their
comments, the band stomping so long an introduction that I
eventually realize this isn't a song with accompaniment so much
as an instrumental 'novelty' with vocal obbligato. When I have
almost given up expecting him, in mid-phrase Perry enters,
suave and witty, magically syncopated. He floats across the
barlines, his accents never coinciding with the strong beat. The
backing group comes in, preppy male voices da-da-da-ing and
la-la-la-ing at twice the speed of Perry, even as he croons at a
slower speed than the orchestra. It is as though three distinct
layers of time co-exist; just as the time of the disc's making, its
lease of playing-life in Church Avenue, and the nostalgic
entrancement of this present moment co-exist and coalesce in
my mind as I listen. Brittle and vulnerable it may be, but the
disc accretes time, lives, human generations.

On automatic the discs clonk down the metal spindle one
after another. I forget what I have chosen for the stack and
familiar songs come round again and again: 'Chi-Baba Chi-
Baba', 'White Christmas', 'Myself When Young', 'White
Christmas', all uncannily free of repeating grooves. The uncanny
strikes me more forcibly, though, when, back in the room after

a brief absence during which the music has continued, I have a sudden, cold prevision of a time when the discs will still be sweetly spinning though all the actors of the piece are dead.

*

We have completed our game of Newmarket and our reminiscences of Victor and begun to gather up our presents. Grandma's genial grandmotherly radiance fills the room. Even peaky Aunty Gladys looks moderately rosy, suffused by the heat, the sociability, the food and drink. She offers everyone a last cup of tea and goes into the kitchen to brew it. She fits so snugly into this house that I can barely imagine her in any other place; and, indeed, she suffers from an agoraphobic reluctance to go into town or further afield than the nearest corner shop, on Bridson Street. One Sunday afternoon she did take me and my sister off into an unfamiliar reach of Buile Hill Park, the part where it shades into Seedley Park. There we found a bustling crowd of hatted promenaders and perched with sunbathers on a slope – it all seemed staggeringly new! – and were gorged with toffees and lollies. Otherwise I have never seen her off these solid premises.

And never shall again. Though her precarious health is assiduously invigilated by Uncle Dick with his homeopathic nostrums and black molasses, there will come a time when she needs the stiffer treatments and will get to the proper doctors too late. Dick will never forgive them their negligence, their culpable mediocrity, as he sees it; no more than Victor ever ceased to bemoan the failure of those Shanghai physicians to act fast enough for little Jackie. Here, then, a wicked symmetry.

Uncle Richard will live on, a drily reclusive sceptic, housed with Grandma – least lonely of widows – and Uncle Jack, and in due course just with the latter, in a council prefab not far from here. Behind a still more prolific tangle of privets than before, he will continue his quiet researches into various subjects, not only the mysteries of health but (for instance) the mischiefs and hypocrisy of politicians as evidenced by their appearances on television programmes, which he wryly videos. He will always remain studiously unshocked by the world's wickednesses.

By then, of course, the indifferent motorway traffic will have long been hurtling through Aunty Gladys's steam-filled kitchen and this sitting room so alive with talk, bestrewn with Christmas wrappings.

'I do wish I could have a saxophone too,' I whiningly reiterate to my mother, as I hand her the *Lady and the Tramp* Disney annual which is one of my actual presents, and Gladys passes round a plate of biscuits.

'Oh give over with you!' Grandma scolds me, with a burst of wild high-pitched laughter. 'You want the world!'

'Can I play with the sewing machine then?'

And I make do with a quick burst on the wrought-iron treadle of the Singer that lives in a wooden hood below one of the windows looking on to the darkened alley. First your feet have to heave, then the mechanism speeds up under its own momentum, the hand-wheel races round, the cotton-hook twitches and the wide-eyed needle stabs down. I fantasize that I'm pedalling a paddle-boat in the dark harbour waters of Hong Kong, just for a minute.

Cups of tea are being slurped behind me, the adults chat on. Joey, usually so voluble, is dropping asleep on Aunty Pat's ashy lap.

'Come on, we're ready to go,' my mother announces.

The coats are fetched. We say our thank-yous and goodbyes and I'm excited because I know at any moment coins will be surreptitiously pressed into us children's palms. Though Uncle Dick is not a man inclined to spend money he never fails to stump up for us at the end of our visits. I'm embarrassed about revealing my expectation but careful not to put myself out of generosity's reach.

'Here y'a,' Uncle Dick says in an undertone, squeezing my hand, half-smiling, avoiding my eye as I walk into the hall. There Aunty Gladys makes a similiar generous gesture, as does Uncle Jack with a grin, Grandma with a kiss. I don't notice the other quick and intimate transactions besides my own. The front door is thrown open. We are standing on the step saying more goodbyes and wishing everyone a happy new year. The big street-numerals seem to glow in the dark.

'Toodle pip!' calls Grandma.

'Toodle pip!' echoes Uncle Richard, still neat in collar and tie, waving.

'Bye-bye! B'bye!'

'B'-bye!'

'Happy New Year!'

Tucked into the back of the car, I feel a warm satiate delight running through my body, and my head is full of tunes and images – images of travel, of possibility. We curve back up Weaste Lane. The park looks just as dark but less inhospitable than before. We cross Eccles Old Road and climb up Claremont Road into our own territory. My father asks how much money we were given and is impressed when I re-count my coins and tell him.

I am a rich boy.

In a Northern Market

a snapshot in November

Great wrought-iron Victorian canopy liveried in red and gold. A north wind slices through the ranks of outdoor stalls. The faces of folks are raw and ruddy, the shouts of vendors full of rude vigour:

'A pounda mush' for sixty, ladies!' goes one.

'Oo wants five pounds o' my best bananas forra pound?' goes another.

The curious adjacency to Tesco's, just a ramp and trolley conveyor belt away: as though it has been decreed there shall be two orders of shopping. But up there the emotional tone is flat, the atmosphere sterile, with none of the Open Market's thick vernacular energy, its openness in truth!

'Thank yo'!'

'Thank yo'!'

Everywhere I hear that distinctive local vowel. Though not from the brusque young fellow at the outdoor refreshments wagon, who merely growls:

'Tea should be cheaper than coffee!'

'Nah,' the raw-nosed girl in the van replies. 'Our coffee should be dearer!'

But she serves me a feeble cup of tea.

*

59

Stalls laden with rolls of fabric; strewn with cheap cassettes or Christmas trinkets or children's shoes; stacked with stationery or yams. I'm amused by a sign on the confectionery table saying 'BEST SIDE'. Is it really so? I inquire.

'Yes. But Craven's are over there and they're the *very* best.'

The sales lady, one of a brisk but kindly team of four, states her opinion unanswerably. I root through the trays and jars to find the superlative Craven's label. Even the good stuff looks tired, but the sweets on the disadvantaged side look positively second-hand, and oh the biscuits! square tinsful of dryness incarnate: squashed and faded Jaffa Cakes, unbreakable fig biscuits, brandy-snaps without a hint of glamour!

Nearby are a fishmonger and a butcher, their wares slapped down like a challenge on the marble benchtops, and knives at the ready. Tucked into a corner is the tripe stall. It's evidently been a good day for tripe, only a single piece remains: white wrinkled skin, like a polystyrene imitation of itself, yet still vaguely obscene. From a few steps away I peer as if at an alien organism, but the tripe lady peers at me peering, not purchasing, and doesn't seem to approve.

*

What a human cornucopia! what jollity! I think as I stroll the length and breadth and diagonals of the market. And what desolation here when it's not a market day! Then the great iron structure becomes a mausoleum. But for now the festivity breezes on. An icepick of a wind from Siberia cuts my face as I re-enter the outside section, where a fruit stall is evidently packing up.

'Are you closin' already?' somebody asks.

'Aw yeah!' says the stocky vendor. 'It's bin a cracker today! I dorn't know where thiv all come from today! We've 'ad them standin' on th'ir 'eads.'

An elderly turbanned man ambling past smiles and repeats the question.

'Plenty soon finish?'

'Yeah,' comes the nonchalant reply. 'Plenty soon finish today.'

The familiar but these days increasingly rare aroma of pipe tobacco wafts across from a man seated behind a table on which a diversity of scissors is laid out with an almost scholarly care. I relish the neatly lathed little bowl into which he is so unapologetically puffing – he evokes a vanishing world of stiff-backed uncles – and notice from their cardboard packaging that all the scissors have come from the Canary Isles.

Why on earth the Canary Isles?

A hefty, smooth-talking fellow behind a stall piled with linoleum scrolls professionally opines to a lady customer:

'That one 'ould definitely look better, I'll be't first to admit. So when it comes in, I'll give you a ring. 'Ave I got your number?'

(Lino is so boring, I think.)

And that fruit and veg man is still going at it, the round-shouldered Pennines mistily looming behind him, his unshaven, frost-nibbled features quite luridly animated as he emits his cry:

'Pounda mushrooms sixty, ladies!'

And again:

'Pounda mush, ladies, for only 60p!'

Adventure of Dwelling

... poetically, man/ Dwells ...

– Hölderlin

The sun dapples the prolific tree-cover of residential Manor Road, you are ambling towards your dumped bike in the brown buckled sandals of those days, the sticky remains of an ice-cream cone on your hand, two and threepence in the pocket of your summer shorts – your spends minus the ice-cream. It is the summer holidays, time of adventure. The Saturday after-noon is vast and skyey, town as still as countryside, the houses as though uninhabited, the pavement burning.

You don't remark it, but the air is full of the scent of roses, cut grass, nettles – thick summer smells, with a tincture of tar. You feel you could ride well out of bounds today; but you just sit down on a kerbstone by the grammar school playing-fields, mystically quiet.

*

This area of Salford 6, bisected by the winding, declining Claremont Road, and narrowing to the high apex of the Height 'triangle' – an apex that can be touched in all its literalness of geometry, in the form of a hardware shop's absurdly sharp triangular edge – used to be populated by the very rich. Lord

62

Palmerston planted an oak in what is now a corner of Lullington Road. He was staying with the influential, philanthropic Misses Heywood at the ample establishment known as Claremont. Presently it was demolished, and the ladies moved a few yards across their land to the large house of Chaseley, which they at once renamed Claremont.

That went, too, and the grammar school was ultimately built on the land vacated. But the neighbouring house, Chaseley Field, remains; as does Buile Hill – now a mining museum – in the park of that name opposite; and the refurbished, battle-mented Summer Hill, formerly part of the girls' high school, set to become an old people's home. Chaseley, a medium sized but roomy edifice, best preserves the memory of what the area was like when dotted by millionaire's mansions. Secretive, imposing behind their protective walls, shrubs and trees; dour but entic-ing, mysterious: new spaces of being.

*

You cycle along Doveleys Road to Rivington Manor. This house, built for the wealthy Pilkingtons, shouldn't be confused with Rivington Pike, the stumpy trig point of the moors near Horwich, goal of countless Sunday outings. Every childhood has its double Rivingtons.

Rivington Manor stands at the end of a gloomy avenue in a small park – well, very small by park standards, but huge by private garden standards – a spinney through which you can pick your curious way unnoticed. Not that there ever seems anyone in the house to notice you; it always offers a bleakly silent countenance to the world, but you know it is not uninhabited. A strangely thin, strange-talking, dark-blonde girl in your class resides there. Amazingly, she is taken to school and collected each day by taxi. She seems like an eccentric aunt before her time. She is impressive because she lacks friends yet never shows signs of loneliness.

Steep-roofed, high-gabled, the house has a cool, withdrawn air, like the girl. Even on a blazing July afternoon, it seems to have been raining in the region of the house. You hardly dare look through the windows, but dart round to the back and over the wall, jumping down on to a grass mound from which you can see far across the county – as far, you fancy, as the other Rivington.

You descend to Cholmondeley Road and cross to the grander Chomlea Manor. 'Cholmondeley' is correctly pronounced – useful schoolboy information this – 'Chomlea'. So there are two Chomleas as well. It occupies a plot easily big enough for a housing estate, which is what it will become. A magically mouldering place, enclosed within walls low enough positively to invite trespass. No one, you suspect, lives here, though the lodge is used as a tennis clubhouse, as you well know, and there are wire-netted shale courts below the crumbling terraces and parterres. You snoop with more effrontery than at Rivington. Chomlea is more open and feels safer if more exotic, ancient.

The old pile is such a familiar feature of Claremont Road, visible from the road, unthinkingly regarded on every car journey, that however exotic it might prove on closer investigation, you would accept it as inevitable; yet it belongs to a far different world from Harold Macmillan's Britain with its jingly ice-cream vans. A bit Elizabethan perhaps? Italianate? Ghosts, in any case, are said to cluster in the cold public alley on the far side of the grounds; and if no ghosts, then definitely trees marching on the shivery autumn nights.

*

The alley will retain its ghostliness and the new houses and flats won't efface something recognizable, evocative in the contour of the land; the big-eaved lodge will be kept as a private residence. Rivington will seem the more thoroughly expunged, for all that the low soot-coloured wall and its gatestone carved with *Rivington* will survive and an outer ring of swaying trees. The brute apartment blocks to be built here will bear no trace of the mystic past.

In your teens, despondent on a love-quest, you will climb (interloper of the sunny afternoon) the stone steps of new Rivington to an advantageous third-floor balcony, hoping for a glimpse of the beloved in a back-garden of the nearby road. You'll see nothing. But through a window flung open for summer, you'll hear somebody playing Debussy's piano prelude, *La Fille aux cheveux de lin*, the pure phrases let down gently into the air to float, linger and fade. Nobody about but yourself, transfixed to the burning stone, as though waiting for something to happen. A time of *advent*-ure.

*

And you'll trudge up Claremont Road, much later, in the heat, glumly, but noticing as for the first time how each of the ordinary houses is brimful of significant character. Each front garden bears a secret signature; that permanently, shockingly overgrown one in front of a window showing dirty shredded curtains and a dusty bowl of plastic flowers and clock is merely the most obvious case of differentiation. The dullest dwelling in your area wears a singular expression. Each identical dormer window glows uniquely in the sky. The most boring brick gatepost proclaims *here* and not another place, *now* and not another time. That tightly serrated jet-black door-knob thrusting itself forward on the doctor's surgery door! What could be more *unalike*?

*

But for now you merely find your bicycle and pedal furiously home. And you still have money in your pocket.

That Interface

an epigram

Slice your balls they would, if they got you in a dark corner, down Cross Lane way, which is the worst, those Salford lads, if you happened to be on the wrong side of them, as how could you not be – violin-case-carrying, games-dodging, 'sensitive', they'd love you! But you weren't particularly afraid, life went on as normal, didn't it, despite such nasty rumours. It was a terrible thought all the same: a punishment like *that*? The extremity of it meant you had to think of school bullying in a new way, as something deadly, unspeakably serious. It was already an alarming enough prospect, scrotum-tightening if not worse.

Jed Hollings was the leading figure, the indisputably toughest, nastiest boy in his year, with a cadre of henchmen and a network of more or less uneasy sympathizers, and no one really to challenge him. He had a brutish baby face, thick lips, a sallow complexion; was stockily, pugnaciously built, not tall. He had a rough, intimidating accent, with a certain huskiness to it; but although his mother was poor, he was decently dressed, his green blazer much less scruffy than that of his weasel-faced lieutenant. The very name inspired fear: Jed Hollings. He and his cronies would 'sort you out'. The police had been into the school more than once to sort *him* out.

It was the spring of 1968, you were fourteen. You bussed to Central Library most Saturday afternoons and wandered round town. One day a university student with much longer hair than yours tried to sell you a rag mag. 'There's a long poem by W. H. Auden in it,' went the sales talk, and quickly you were persuaded. You turned to the poem, you couldn't believe your eyes: 'It was a spring day, a day for a lay, when the air/Smelled like a locker-room, a day to blow or get blown.' – So you'd been tricked! It was just a pornographic spoof. But no it wasn't. It was your first taste of the nineteen-sixties. And Market Street seemed to give way under your feet.

You were living on a sheer interface of banal school bullying and unheard-of liberation. Something was approaching which would light up that dark intimidated provincial corner with a tremendous flash. The harsh threats of a Salford accent would be no more. Of course you did not know this. But next time you came eye to eye with Jed Hollings, at an after-school function where his mother was present – you were surprised how young and attractive she was, how *respectable* – he seemed oddly softer than before. He even half-grinned at you. When he said something to his mother, you noticed for the first time that he had a slight lisp. You saw that his lips were like Mick Jagger's.

THREE

Avatars of Genius

. . . a genius temperament ought to be handled with care

– Robert Lowell, *History*

ONE

A Golden Dream of Art

One of the great events of my adolescence was discovering the idea of genius. Even in earlier childhood this notion had somehow taken hold of me as though synonymous with life itself, with all its best excitements. In the playground of my primary school I inveigled out of Peter Mann repeated, varied admissions that I was, and had to be, a genius. Coyly I pooh-poohed the idea, the very idea, only to drink in a deeper satisfaction with each of his fresh insistences. It did strike a less vain part of me that these assurances were remarkably polite, *decent*; but I had small notion of flattery or what it meant to be politic; nor, I think, did he. There was an awkward irony in the situation – for he was certainly more of a genius than I. Though I was a few months older and technically a year ahead of him – and it was thus seemly that he deferred to me to celebrate *my* genius – he was nonetheless in my class, having skipped a year;

71

and as if that were not a sufficient demonstration of genius, of his ascendancy, he had recently pipped me for the top mark in a composition exercise and had the galling (to me) distinction of having his piece read aloud by our teacher. How crisply, concisely written it was, how vivid! He'd employed a phrase – *jet-black hair* – which I'd never come across but thought terrific. Subsequently I examined his script, admiring the decisive, mature hand, dearly wishing I'd written the thing myself. I doubted I could compete, and mentally shelved the whole business, hoping to resume without delay the subject of my own genius. He was sheer modesty standing there in the bricked corner of our playground, where we two weren't 'playing' in the usual rough and tumble sense but certainly playing with ideas, even risking the odd intellectual bruise. Despite my buoyant ego, I wasn't necessarily convinced by my own cool acceptance of supremacy. I wondered whether all this talk of genius wasn't a hopeless charade.

In the bosom of my family my status as a genius could find its easy consolation. I was only too ready to amuse my parents and their friends proudly parroting my wordy definitions of scientific terms. '*Viscosity* is the tendency of liquid or gas to resist by internal friction the relative motion of its molecules and hence any change of shape; the magnitude of this, as measured by the force per unit area resisting a flow in which parallel layers unit distance apart etc. etc.,' I'd rattle off like Pozzo's Lucky. I was altogether a boy of words – long ones, of course, such as *palaeontological*, such as *intrinsically*. Once, a boy in the Cubs with me, who happened to be a genius himself, gifted as he was with a preternaturally mellifluous treble, berated me as I was swinging on the iron gates of the Congregational church in whose grounds our meetings were held, saying: 'What makes you think you're so clever? Do you know what those words *mean*?' He wasn't physically aggressive but his passionate scorn gave me pause, an early inkling of the dangers of pretentiousness, of outrageous phoneyness. I *did* know the meanings of words, by and large; and I knew them intimately in the sense that my words were personal friends, big companionable entities which I could roll with me wherever I went. But sometimes I feared I simply wasn't clever enough. Returning late back to school one lunchtime, I was less troubled by lateness than by the fact that my mother had been demurring in a conversation about whether I would eventually get to Oxford. Whereas it had seemed inconceivable to my youthful vanity that I should not, I now abruptly accepted a lowered, mediocre view of myself. I would just have to be an ordinary schoolboy after all.

Such delusions of ordinariness never lasted long. I would soon be back with my dreams of great achievement, of fabulous discovery, of what I was unable then to identify as aesthetic bliss, a thirst for which undoubtedly drove me in most of my outgoings to the world. My interest in natural history now seems to me clearly to have been a lust for the paraphernalia of collecting and exhibiting specimens rather than commitment to science *per se* (though arguably a genuine scientific passion begins in this way too). I collected all categories of specimens – butterflies, moths, beetles, even flies; flowers, shells, fossils, minerals; even de-fleshed the odd sheep's skull. Butterflies – symbol of the aesthetic experience at its purest and most joyous – were my first love; and flutteringly alive or fixed in scholar's cabinets, they still afford me stabs of unique pleasure. My strongest, strangest pseudo-scientific obsession in those days was what I trumpeted to the world as 'freshwater ecology': the study of ponds, with for me a special reference to the chemical analysis of the water. Not that I ever succeeded in performing such analysis; but I constantly dreamt of doing so, using the apparatus – a mysterious crate of test-tubes, titration tubes, pipettes, reagents – which I had coveted in one of the many scientific catalogues for which I was forever brazenly sending off. The water-analysis outfit became a myth of of my child-hood, the greatest possible benison, an image of unattainability (far too expensive even for birthday and Christmas presents combined). Without the precious box – so much more aesthet-ically satisfying than the highest grade of toyshop chemistry set – I nonetheless set myself up as a water analyst armed with a rudimentary pH tester for gardening and what bits of tubes and chemicals I could muster, together with the invaluable hand-book published by the Freshwater Biological Association of Ambleside. *Some Methods of Water Analysis for Limnologists* I cherished inordinately, as a book in its own right, a handsome literary artefact. It may not have been a title to light the skies, but the thick and stylishly printed pamphlet on whose red cover it appeared was to my mind a work of such aesthetic perfection that I scarcely allowed myself to touch it, let alone read it. Reading it wasn't quite the point; acceding to its luminous authority over all the world was.

Whenever I could persuade my father, or even a friend's father, to drive me there, I'd plant myself on the bank of one of the drab ponds dotted across the flatlands of east Lancashire – Swinton Fields, Chat Moss – and undertake in imagination a full-scale ecological survey (with chemical analysis) of the poor little patch. I had a metal-framed plankton net with thick glass tube tied to the aperture of the bolting silk cone and would shove it through the silt and detritus of the murky bottom. Usually my 'sample' consisted of nothing interesting to the naked eye at all; at best I'd secure a water boatman, dapper little bug, rowing itself up and down the cloudy tube. The expeditions invariably subsided into a feeling of contingency, impotence and cold. How small and slight the living pond was after my glamorous scientific expectations of it! How hopeless the task of surveying it, and how tedious! How paltry the specimens! The dream of aesthetic satisfaction had foundered, just as the beautiful concept of a book may tarnish in the writer's mind as he sets to the raw labour of devising its actual sentences. My father, glad I'd again wearied of this strange pursuit, would drive us both home.

But my unlikely genius for water analysis stood me in good stead in a weekend scouting competition in a wood near Worsley where we were required to pretend we were colonizing another planet. With our scanty resources – tent, knife, billycan – we had to establish a secure base from which to assess the 'alien' environment. What could be more appropriate than a spot of authentic water analysis! I went round the available streams siphoning off samples, fiddled plausibly with my mock implements, threw in a few innocuous chemicals, and paraded the results before the veteran scouters who came to examine us. I eloquently put it to them that such scientific recourse was inescapable in the circumstances. And we won the trophy! Our scout pack, though lively, wasn't renowned for competitive prowess and my comrades in their euphoria held me mainly responsible for their success. The crackling campfire, smell of woodsmoke, became associated in my mind with a friendly sense of victory. I realized that one's wits, one's genius, could be a socially useful instrument.

To earn this gratifying attention I hadn't really had to take the stage. I'd made a 'public' effect simply by being myself, operating behind the scenes in the cunningly effective manner of creative artists, be they writers, painters or composers. This I found appealing, though earlier in childhood I'd been sufficiently

allured by the direct public approach. Jolly compère aged ten
of a children's revue at a holiday camp in Sussex, I cracked bad
jokes in a fresh northern accent, having taken the microphone
with the unpractised ease of a fairly natural extrovert, confident
of approval. Later, I would decide to renounce extroversion
quite consciously in favour of a proto-adolescent inwardness,
shyness, cussedness even. For the moment I thrived as a
dynamic, if asthma-prone, little virtuoso, twirling my cane of
childish charm, knowing how to regale my audience. And it was
on this summer holiday that my interest in playing the violin
was definitively aroused. Some months before, I'd overheard
the sounds of the solo instrument at a friend's house when his
father put on a record of, I think, *Scheherazade* or possibly *Swan
Lake*, both of which contain a violin obbligato; and been
amazed. Here was something new under the sun! Newness in
the pure state; as though I'd been spoken to in French or
German and – fantasy of the lifelong mediocre linguist! –
instantly been able to understand what was said. The toy
instruments – trombone, saxophone, guitar – to which I'd been
so powerfully attracted as a young child now looked puny
indeed. This sound was a gorgeous fabric, pure brocade. It was
life. From reading Sherlock Holmes stories I'd derived an exotic
bohemian image of violin-playing; and on the Sussex holiday I
met a man who made my fantasy beguilingly real. This young,
chipper fellow, on holiday alone, taking a lively interest in all
the sports and activities, assured me he could play the violin
and actually had an instrument in his chalet. Somehow I never
got to see it. When we returned north, I would soon be starting
grammar school, and it became my resolute purpose to take
violin lessons immediately I got there.

Signals can come to us at all times literally out of the sky, out
of merely living, as though we were peripatetic radio receivers.

Sometimes they are easily explained. One afternoon many years later I was mooching on the parched slopes of the Athens Acropolis and found myself repeatedly wafted back to those first days of violin lessons, to the school music room and ruddy-faced Mr Aspinall, a gifted player but with his perfect pitch and moody temperament ill-suited to the tuition of small boys dissonant to him in more ways than one. The resin with which we over-zealously primed our junior violin bows he always pronounced 'rosin', and with an unvoiced *r*. Ah, that was it! the smell of resin was everywhere apparent, as the stuff oozed glacially out of the countless pine trunks. Mr Aspinall had in his laconic way twitted me about going on holiday to the Costa Brava one year. I never knew quite why; though it was uncommon in those days for families to take holidays abroad and this had been a bold venture for us, causing me to miss one of his lessons. Now here I was on a more exotic holiday, being returned with a slam of the door into the east wing music room, where we would hang about for an hour or two after school each Friday, taking turns to play our exercises. He would lightly pick out accompanimental chords on the upright if the mood took him: this was a kind of assent. In other moods he glared at us in disbelief. I always longed for him to take a fiddle himself. He rarely condescended to, but when he did my heart leapt at the fabulous sound he unthinkingly made, at the result produced by that elusive, madly desired accomplishment, vibrato.

One summer I practised harder than ever, hurling myself at the instrument in my bedroom every day (what my mother and the neighbour must have endured!), until glimmering intimations of vibrato started to occur. I forced it and forced it and doubtless did it all wrong, but I definitely had something to offer Mr Aspinall when the new term began. Will I feel a warmer glow of pleasure than when Mr Aspinall, visibly startled, expressed his satisfaction at my progress? How I'd come on, he exclaimed, and invited the others in the room to listen to how I did it. They were scarcely, of course, swooning over me, but they couldn't deny the vibrato *fact*. That was virtually a quantifiable achievement, the only sort that schoolboys recognize. And I knew that my assiduous practice had brought about a genuine upsurge of musicality, beyond the requirements of showing-off. There was a difference in the way I heard things. What had been beyond my aural grasp started into clarity. The note-patterns seemed simpler, the rhythms more manageable, the music altogether less *black*. It was the same a few years later when, desperate at lacking so fundamental a musical skill, I simply made myself play the piano, and practically all at once the lower-stave notes governed by the hitherto cryptic bass clef were as easy to read as ABC. Only the viola's C clefs were a problem after that; and to this day I have to think before deciphering a note under their governance. Thus I preserve a sense of what it is like *not* to be able to read music.

Soon I was playing in the school orchestra. Conducted by the music master, Mr Blackford, we enhanced the hymn-singing of Thursday morning assemblies and usually offered a modest item of our own, perhaps the arrangement of Handel's *March from Scipio* by David Stone or that arrangement of Mozart fragments which was just called *Fantasie*. The spelling and pronunciation of this clipped title intrigued me: not *Fantasia*, simple and exotic, nor *Fantasy*, simple and prosaic; but the awkward, obscure word with the final, foreign -*ie*. I assumed that Mozart himself had written the piece until eventually I heard the overture to *The Marriage of Figaro* and realized that its main tune was none other than that of our poor provincial *Fantasie*. Nervously attempting the second violin part with my friend David Forrester at the same desk, helping each other to avoid false entries and the doubling or halving of the tempo (a major weakness of mine), I had my first experiences of what orchestral ensemble was like, how an orchestra sounded from within. I perceived harmony and counterpoint as they came to life through the meeting of parts which were not, as on the keyboard, picked out by a pair of hands and made to seem a single inevitable entity, but hazardously embodied in the mouths and messy hands of schooboys each of whom was all too distinctive in appearance and personality. Thus the flute for me will always be inseparable from the name Frederick Solomon – and even from the name of the Cambridge college to which, to my admiration, and with an air of quiet, slightly epicene efficiency, he in due course went up, there to read Natural Sciences and for all I know abandoning the instrument for ever. The violin is personified not by my immediate contemporaries who fiddled but by a debonair boy two years above me called John Clayton: he was the leader of our little band, rarely more than ten players strong.

But I certainly didn't find the piano lacking in interest. When Mr Blackford gave a solo during Thursday asssembly, I would stare from my orchestral seat at the magical movements of his hands, his hairy but flexible wrists, the sinuous pattern made by the depressions of the keys, and wish the masterful performance, beyond my wildest hopes of emulation, would never stop. Chopin's *Fantasie-Impromptu* – that word again! – which he frequently rendered, struck me as the most amazing and ingenious music ever devised: I could scarcely credit either that one could have the dexterity to play rhythms in four against rhythms in six at the requisite speed, or that those black and abstract skeins of notes, so like the driest of studies on the page, could through the interaction of the two parts yield so much quick and glinting melodic life. The two hands, in their laundered

Thursday morning cuffs, imminently to be relegated to chalk and blackboard, were distinctly working a miracle: two hands making a musical effect unmistakably in three dimensions; the secular miracle of art by which a wonderful, utterly unpredictable but inevitable object is created. I was always hoping for Mr Blackford to play for us during proper music lessons, which easily lapsed into aridity; but he resisted our clamorous requests with a kind of coyness; just as, when it came to playing gramophone records for us as an end of term treat, he would invariably pique us by saying we could have anything, 'But don't ask me to put on the *1812* overture.'

One of his private piano pupils was John Clayton. His fingers on the keyboard were magical too: he was suaver in manner than his teacher, self-possessed in performance to a degree, and had been so even at the junior school he and I and Forrester and Peter Mann all shared, where he was already taking solo spots during the morning hymns there. If anyone was a genius, he was. I found disconcerting traces of his genius all over the grammar school. In the geography room, for instance, his amazing maps of the world were pinned to the wall; assignments executed with such abnormal finesse – the outlines unerringly drawn, the bold colours perfectly mixed, the italic calligraphy thrillingly novel and peculiarly *virile* – that one felt the burden of one's own childish clumsiness and messiness with redoubled acuteness, and just knew that one was going to be stuck with it for some time yet. John Clayton had broken out of the ugly chrysalis of adolescent awkwardness, or else had somehow been a butterfly from the start. Naturally, I wanted to draw expert maps myself. I promptly acquired a fountain pen with italic nib and set about the sincerest form of flattery. But there was going to have to be a great deal of flattery. I should also need to improve my dress, thicken my tie-knot, maintain a neat crease in my trousers, and mend my complexion: John Clayton's had a quasi-rouged, powdery texture, and no spots. I should have to do outstandingly well in every academic subject, play the violin rather better than I did, learn to play the piano, write poetry – he'd had a clutch of poems published in the annual school magazine – and even, yes, write music! I'd have to change my deportment and my demeanour.

Suddenly I was living only to resemble John Clayton, and possibly – it seemed a more remote than hubristic notion – surpass him. Under the crushing impact of his superiority it was that I took that decision – sitting back reflectively during a pause in an orchestral rehearsal, I remember – to cultivate shyness and introversion just like his. Each fresh evidence of his remarkable abilities alarmed and fascinated me. Would the agenda of my keeping-up, my willed transformation, ever be finally set? I opened the new edition of the school magazine with trepidation. Heaven forbid there should be more of his poems – and there were! And they were brilliant! For someone in the Education Office had published a report on local school-children's literary activities and had said so: *brilliant* was the word, nor did I doubt its truth. The poems dazzled and ravished me – the imaginative leaps even of their titles; the new areas of experience annexed (the author had been on a school trip to Italy and brought back verses evoking the quiet stone cool of a villa in the Veneto); the formal daring (free verse in bold swatches, line-breaks that took the breath away); the vigorous sap of the vocabulary; the sheer newness of it all. In the exhilaration of John Clayton's style, which both continued and surpassed that of his italic calligraphy, I found new modes of being; as though his were the one irresistible poetry there had ever been, with the magic word spoken in due time. The very pretentiousness of the free-verse posture was lifeblood to me, and I pored again and again over the section of the magazine that contained these precious utterances, vocables of the now. Of course I started to write poetry myself, but my work struck me as phoney by the side of John Clayton's; my own pretentiousness appealed to me less. In time I adroitly secured for myself the editorship of the school magazine and shamelessly printed a long sequence of my own poems to line up with my 'rival'. But it only seemed like cheating.

My rival I did not actually meet for some months after my intellectual infatuation with him began. His natural shyness, which so impressed me, and my acquired version of the same thing would have logically contrived to keep us apart, but I expected I'd barely been noticed by him. Why should I have been? I was two years younger, a kid who played second violin, while he played piano solos in assembly, published 'brilliant' poetry and – his most overwhelming achievement – was a real composer of music. Perhaps the other distinctions might have been assimilated more or less comfortably by his admiring inferiors such as myself, if only he had not also possessed the uncanny ability to hear music in his head and accurately notate it. How could this be? The rest of us were still learning how to read music, how to make adequate sense of that black dizziness of dots, while he was manifestly thinking in musical language, living and breathing it. I forget how I discovered about his composing; rumour, I suppose, of the same breathless sort that alleged he could write down without trouble anything he heard played, however complex. He'd apparently done arrangements for an out-of-school jazz band by transcribing directly from 78s. Those ticklishly difficult O-level class dictation exercises were risible to him. He had composed, I gathered, a great number of piano pieces; but his first real creative impact on us was made, absurdly enough, by a full-blown orchestral piece.

TWO

A Tyro Like Myself

In our district a youth orchestra was started for the first time. Instrumental tuition given by peripatetic specialists such as Mr Aspinall, leading easy but unfocused lives, wandering from school to school, had flourished in the country to such an extent that the least likely areas were plausible catchment for fledgling orchestras. There would generally be a shortage of violas, a desk too few of cellos, an absent second oboe, but passable bands were being easily mustered in education authorities throughout the land. We were one of a host set up in the Manchester region, each a modest mimicry of Sir John Barbirolli's Hallé Orchestra in the specific sense that wartime stringencies had obliged Barbirolli to recruit from a pool of amateurs and bandsmen sometimes not much more experienced than school-kids, and in the very church and school halls we ourselves used for rehearsals.

Our educational authority had a sympathetic and enterprising chief music organizer in Michael Baker, who had come north to take up his post and whose southernish, or at any rate Midlands-ish speech beguiled us. It was the beginning of an era. Mr Baker invited his heads of music to send their tolerably able instrumentalists on a week's course at one of the nicer secondary schools during an Easter vacation. I turned up nervously on a fresh Tuesday morning and was given a place in the second violins. Grouped in pairs at our tubular music-stands on the assembly hall's scuffed parquet we tackled the 'Entrance and March of the Peers' from *Iolanthe* and simplified versions of

Bizet's *L'Arlésienne* suite and Chabrier's *Marche joyeuse* with our wonderfully clumsy ensemble, uncertain rhythm and whining intonation. They were scrannel sounds we made, to be sure; though at the parental concert ending the week it was resolved to perpetuate the orchestra. John Clayton was our leader: he had the steadiest sense of rhythm of any of us. He and his fellow firsts were in another league than me. As yet a plodder but for all my affected shyness always hoping to make an impression one way or another, I accepted my lot, enjoyed the company of the amiable buffoons on the front desk of the seconds, and mooched off during a couple of the lunch hours across the nearby park with an invigorating sense of what it was to be engaged on a worthwhile project, and therefore relishing the breaks all the more keenly. Down in the distance I could make out the Manchester Ship Canal and all its industrial complication of chimneys, derricks, refineries: a somehow inspiriting vista that sent me back to the rehearsal hall in a state of welling creative excitement. I resined – or rosined – my bow for the afternoon session with a vengeance.

The youth orchestra became a Saturday morning routine. I got to know John Clayton better while still scarcely ever talking to him. His utter composure always impressed me: not only was he blessedly exempt from the physical messiness and ungainliness customary to adolescence, but even in negotiating what to us were the trickiest pages of music – negotiating them, as leader, on our behalf as well as his own – he would sit demurely, cheeks a handsome ruddy, posture elegant and musically effective, with perhaps the merest tightening of lips to attest to effort. Comparatively, I was in a perpetual funk. I tried to profit from his example, and at least improve my sense of rhythm, whose inadequacy was humiliatingly evident in sectional rehearsals. I did have my vibrato to fall back on, of course; I produced a better tone than most of the others, including John. Whether or not he had acquired the trick of it – it would be astonishing if there was this thing he could not do – he did not make that kind of effect. Perhaps he disliked such voluptuousness, genuinely preferring his own fine thread of tone, forever linked in my memory with the poignant first violin obbligati in Mozart's clarinet quintet, as performed at one of our school's Christmas concerts. Yes, John Clayton's sound could be said to be tinny. He wasn't, then, a natural violinist, just a natural pianist – and composer.

Soon he produced his *Italian Rhapsody* for us to play. Mr Baker announced wryly one morning that we would try out a piece by Clayton and passed round the composer's hand-copied parts. I secretly gasped with admiration as we ran through the piece. It was rhythmic, tuneful, catchy, very neatly devised and, though modest in length and scope, tinged with originality. I, at any rate, had never heard anything that sounded quite like it. I clearly remember it still – the skipping principal rhythm, that flute melody, breathily taken by buxom and sophisticated Marge Wisbech (Frederick Solomon having departed for higher education). The piece seemed to have depths and subtleties in excess of its simple binary form and conventional genre. I decided I would have to learn to compose something of my own like this.

The months went by. We moved our youth orchestra base twice, to a leafily secluded adult education centre then to a prison-like secondary school on a concrete yard next to the rugby club. On Saturday mornings we traipsed here bleary-eyed and often enough in winter with hands too frozen to play the violin: numb fingers on the steel E string gave that horrible burning sensation. We began each session with sectionals, first and second violins separate, cellos, flutes, clarinets and so on, each group being dragged through their parts in a cold classroom by a 'peripatetic'. At mid-morning we'd queue up in one of the larger classrooms for coffee, biscuits and chat: a twenty-minute break that for most of us was the social fulcrum of the week. The full orchestra would finally assemble for the main rehearsal under Mr Baker. How many pieces we went through bit by bit, stopping and starting, getting to know the feel of music's nuts and bolts, getting to know each other in this highly specialized way! Romances developed according to what eye-contact was possible from where you sat. Mr Baker would inform us about our up-coming concerts – we'd ventured beyond the immediate area by now, playing as far afield as Leamington Spa, his home town – and joke and sometimes scold us, and of course tune us. He had an acute ear and never failed to impress me with his ready ability to pinpoint the players within the tutti A who were out of tune. 'Second trumpet, a shade flat,' he'd observe. 'Back desk seconds, sharp.' They'd sound another A by themselves and prove him just. (I couldn't always settle whether my own strings were sharp or flat, never mind someone's on the other side of the room.) Then we'd begin the piece. Mr Baker would stop us at once. 'Together!' he'd cry. We'd start again, and totter along for a few minutes, and be stopped. 'Second violins, I know at the back you can't hear the rest of the orchestra. Don't worry if you feel exposed. Play out just the same.' This was an attempt at Prokofiev's March from *The Love for Three Oranges*, of whose dry clops of irony we did not have, I fear, the measure, never mind its filigree string passage work. We'd move on to the manageability of Malcolm Arnold's *Little Suites* or Richard Rodney Bennett's chirrupy *Farnham Festival Overture* or John Dankworth's peculiar piece for narrator and orchestra *Tom Sawyer's Saturday*. How many pieces didn't we attempt! But never my *Pastoral* for orchestra. Never in a month of Saturdays!

For I had indeed found it in myself to compose. Adolescent creative energies are unlimited, and will-power suffices to discover and create talent where not much had been thought to exist. Everyone writes poetry, but I'd even forced myself into the for me less likely domain of the visual arts, even, Lord bless me, trying to sculpt: some futureless blocks of hard stone consequently lay in a corner of my father's garage. The urge to write music became such an overmastering search for a personal identity, a manner of prevailing – rivalry with John Clayton having so goaded me – that music had no choice but to appear, somehow, on the pages of those blue Academy manuscript books I'd so eagerly bought at Forsyth's, the Manchester music store.

Manchester, with its specialist music shops, second-hand record marts such as Gibbs's and the little Avgarde Gallery, with the Hallé, the colleges of music, and above all the Henry Watson Music Library on the second floor of the big-domed Central Library in St Peter's Square, could not have been more nourishing to a hopeful composer. Into the Henry Watson's cornucopia of scores I would dive most Saturday afternoons, after orchestra in the morning and 'dinner' at home. Trips to Manchester were tingling forays into the Creative. I never knew what I'd come back with in my briefcase, heavyish volumes nearly always to the bulky maximum allowance – an Alun Hoddinott piano sonata, a symphony by John McCabe, a new medieval-ish piece by Peter Maxwell Davies – and they would all be sure to find a place in my developing notion of how to write music. Calligraphy itself was a help. Many modern scores were not typeset but published as a facsimile of the original manuscript, and the direct contact thus afforded with a composer's way of doing things, his tics, ingenuities, carelessnesses, was reassuring and emboldening to a tyro like myself. Copying a hand seemed half-way to writing music. Layout on the page, decisions about notation – what precise shapes for note-heads, stems, beams, hairpins – all might be seized and transformed into a personal act or *art*. Anything that came my way was useful. I chanced in the library on Arthur Honegger's *Pastorale d'été* for small orchestra, liked the look of the score, took satisfaction from its brevity, and filched the title (or part of it) for my first go at orchestral writing, my retort to the *Italian Rhapsody*. I never actually heard Honegger's piece; I still haven't – but the old aesthetic pleasure, the appetizing and real possibility of making something of my own, of using a *medium*, suffuses me whenever I catch the glint of that Honegger title in the pages of a newspaper or the *Radio Times*. For a piece surely happens because an artist, however senior, likes to manipulate his medium as a child mudpies, happens not so much in order to fulfil the potential of a soul as that of some interestingly ruled manuscript paper; though it does help if a composer has a good ear.

My orchestral piece followed quickly on the composition of a cumbrous folio of piano pieces, which would have left the listener in no doubt that I couldn't play the instrument; a couple of brief sonatas for solo violin, which did make a sort of sense; a duet for two violins; and the sketch for an organ fantasia intended to evoke the Pennines. Of the *Pastoral*'s content I am surprised I have virtually no memory – but a clear one of the struggle to get it performed, and the *frisson* of joy and embarrassment at finally hearing it, albeit in a single perfunctory run-through. I'd approached Mr Baker with my manuscript, seeking practical advice. He seemed interested, impressed, and had me copy the parts, which he then stacked in the orchestra library, a yellow-painted storeroom at the Music Centre (as the dour edifice had been christened). Each Saturday my heart was set on having my opus rehearsed and collecting a composer's glory; but week after week its airing was deferred. In the pleasantest way Mr Baker always found reasons for putting it off till next week, and I suffered a frustration as messily gnawing as any I've since known. Awkwardly I'd raise the subject, hating to dwell on it, but too piqued to stay silent; galled to be so helplessly dependent on others for my satisfaction. So the *Pastoral* was not to be favoured like the *Italian Rhapsody*; the schedule just wouldn't allow.

Yet one morning after I'd given up weekly hope, when one of the brass peripatetics, Mr Fellowes, was standing in for Mr Baker at the main rehearsal, I was astonished to see my diligently copied parts being handed round and hear the solemn words, 'Now we're going to try a piece written by a member of the orchestra.' I froze with fear and pride and scarcely heard what was duly sounded: my very own crotchets and quavers; my abstract stipulations acquiring material form; the physical secretion, as it were, of my brain; a moulding, however crude, of Time. It was a paltry enough opus, not accomplished like John Clayton's, not memorable – yet not phoney. There was music here, somewhere. I remember the moisture of a flute line and Marge who was kindly playing it – but the rest of the piece is a mental blank. Since the score and parts were long ago mislaid, the music can never now be known or recreated: yet it *existed*. For minutes on a Saturday morning in the 1960s it *was*. I knew what it was to be a composer. I did not receive the plaudits showered on John Clayton. My piece was never again tried out.

Mr Baker never mentioned it, and doubtless it wasn't a very good piece. But I was launched as a composer. I had entered the lists of genius.

Another Mendelssohn?

The rivalry with John Clayton grew more intense within me, though it never seemed that he felt any rivalry with me or surmised my agitations in this department. During a music lesson one day Mr Blackford was teaching us about Felix Mendelssohn, arguably the most prodigious child in the history of composition, surpassing Mozart in the quality of his achievements, if not the quantity. Mr Blackford cited the *Midsummer Night's Dream* overture, put it on the gramophone, and elicited from David Forrester the unhesitating comment, 'Clayton could have done that.' That wasn't what I wanted to hear. John Clayton a second Mendelssohn? I had to chew on that? He'd lately produced a spate of pieces – several piano sonatas, sonatas for oboe and piano and for horn and piano, the beginnings of a proper symphony – and all who had heard a sonata described it as a marvel. John Clayton worked magic with his notes. People believed they had encountered a brand new thing. For myself I rather dreaded hearing the pieces: the new can be scourging. How unpredictable, unaccountable John Clayton truly was! The trouble with living in proximity to him and secretly trying to emulate him was that you never knew what he was cooking. He was not boastful, his achievements would simply emerge. He might be playing the piano to amuse a few friends and without warning slip into a composition of his own. The friends would be mesmerized. Flushed, bashful, he'd admit, 'I wrote that.' Such impromptu recitals were growing all too frequent.

We were going to a country house in Staffordshire for a

youth orchestra 'course'. The bus was due to leave the adult education centre (our erstwhile base) at seven in the June morning and everyone and his parents were bumping about with suitcases and instruments, crunching the gravel of the drive, chatting, enjoying the early breeze. Mr Baker's colleagues were helping to load the coach and trying to solve the inevitable host of minor problems. There was burly, genial Mr Fellowes heaving a double bass on board. There was our tutor for the violin section, Miss Hobson – matey, ironic but considered wildly glamorous – assisting one of the girls in the seconds while laughing with enigmatic Mr Birt, another brass teacher, who had a dapper forelock and a permanent twinkle in his eye and was lugging a kettledrum with the help of Danny McLaughlin, the orchestra's principal percussionist and extrovert. Mr Baker was cheerfully conversing with one of the parents and John Clayton's well-dressed mother sidled up to them. By now most of us were seated on the bus, John Clayton at the front, myself at the back. Then Mr Baker embarked and we pulled off. Seconds, yards, later the bus braked. Mr Clayton was rushing towards us gesticulating with a brown leather music-case in his hand, grinning. John had apparently forgotten his precious manuscripts and his father had slipped back home for them, unbeknown to the composer, who was patently relieved. I was dismayed. I had with me my own small cache of compositions with which I hoped to make a ripple. Alas, the chance of not being grievously upstaged was lost.

The wooden-panelled rooms of Alderley Hall had much cacophony to absorb that week. We ground our way through a charming, obscure concerto grosso by the baroque English composer Richard Mudge, Mr Baker's latest discovery; and let rip with a more obvious Englishry in Vaughan Williams's *English Folksong Suite*, whose jaunty pastoral tones sorted with the greenery visible through the mullioned windows of the house. There were long mysterious corridors here, rooms appearing when you didn't expect them, rumoured secret passages, and a door concealed as a bookcase through which we entered with gleeful impunity. It was in one of the long corridors on a wide window ledge that I had happened to leave some of my manuscripts. Later, during our free time in the afternoon I was startled to hear somebody – it could only be John Clayton – tapping out on the upright piano in the library my little set of variations on *The Daniel Jazz*, a jolly cantata by Herbert Chappell in which I'd sung at school and whose opening piano riff I'd taken for my theme. I barely recognized my poor effort from the baffled sounds he was making and ruefully concluded it was another failed effort – there was no impugning John Clayton's pianism. But it got us talking nearly for the first time. He was cordial, reserved and, I felt, genuinely interested in my stuff. There was a bracing edge to our interchange, a quickly agreed, unspoken readiness to take each other seriously, to strike a mutual pose. There was, too, a mutual shyness and a certain drollery. John Clayton did not generally use a serious social manner. Often he seemed to go as far as he could in the opposite direction, to ingratiate himself as one of the boys and forestall the criticisms of the philistine. Far from affecting a Chopinesque preciosity or arrogance, which would have been wholly plausible, he impressed one with his robustness, down-to-earthness, his populist enthusiasms (such as for Morecambe and Wise). But in this elegant old library he let his cagey artistic side predominate. He asked, 'Can you hear what you write in your head?' and then 'Do you use a piano?' I lied that I could hear it all and truth-told that we didn't have a piano at home. I explained the formal structure of the pieces he had in front of him and he continued trying to read through them. Then I asked him about his work-in-progress, his symphony. He took the manuscript from the leather case. I was deeply impressed. The paper was ruled in twenty-four staves, a very grown-up allowance, and John Clayton had filled several quires with his fastidious notation, altogether an enthralling proposition of newness. A bassoon solo was prominent at the opening, I recall, and there was an extensive obbligato piano part, modelled, as he admitted, on the one in the precocious first symphony of Shostakovich, whom he revered but I scorned for conservatism and bombast. My enthusiasms were more or less avant-garde: the work of Tippett, Maxwell Davies, Stockhausen had come my way. Shostakovich's music seemed old-fashioned and crude in its gestures. (I was unsusceptible then to its irony but probably so was he.) The brilliant craftsmanship and unfailing effectiveness, however slick and ritzy, of a Shostakovich score appealed to John, who was a true showman, whereas I preferred to pose as esoteric intellectual. He regretted his slow progress with the symphony and wondered how fast I composed.

'I wrote a piano sonata in a week,' I informed him. It was true – and I had considered it a rather niggard week at that. 'But it wasn't very good,' I hastened to add.

'I've been struggling with this,' he complained, grasping the manuscript, 'for a year now and still only done twenty pages.'

'Do you compose directly on to full score?' I asked. 'It looks as though you do.'

'Yep.'

'So you don't use sketches?' He shook his head. 'Many composers do, you know,' I said. I'd learned about such matters from an unputdownable book in the Henry Watson Library, *British Composers in Interview*.

I had a twinge of awkwardness at too easily prevailing. My intellectual observations, though risking the fatuous, were meeting no challenge. I felt the mild disconcertment of the loquacious when confronted by the taciturn. For all my programmatic espousal of introversion and shyness, I couldn't match John Clayton's natural reserve, a demeanour suggesting genuine quietude of being. How perfectly composed was this composer! Sitting at the piano he found his most authentic gracefulness, his compact physique wholly apt for and in tune with the instrument. He didn't need to talk to impress and he let me talk, let me feel that I knew much when all the time I knew that he knew more. Physically bigger than John and looming over him, I felt the silent rebuke of his physical exquisiteness. In our few moments of embarrassed silence I glanced out of the window at a lawn and beyond it a patch of woods where yesterday afternoon we'd all been required to play a formal game which I found pointless and exasperating. John Clayton's hands splashed the keyboard. I thought he was going to plunge into a piece of his own or one of the extemporizations he was famous for; but he promptly announced that he had to go and join a group of his peers – my seniors – to play softball. We gathered up our respective works and went our ways. My way was straight back to my dormitory, straight out with a fresh sheet of manuscript and down to the writing of a *pièce d'occasion* I'd just conceived – a skittish set of variations on an English folk-tune for two violins. I planned to ask John Clayton to play it with me and perhaps we could give it at the informal evening concert which would round off the week.

Before that event, however, came the orchestra dance or, as Mr Baker pronounced it, *dahnce*, an occasion which confirmed a side of John Clayton's character I'd only dimly perceived. I dreaded this event, and my racking embarrassment at the prospect must have been apparent, for Mr Baker kindly suggested that I should man the record-player. Feeling foolish,

ever-fearful I would be prised from my safe station, my observation post, I fiddled nervously with the LPs inside their tattered
ballroom-dancing covers, took care with the easily skittering
stylus-arm, and tried to look bright. The waltz, the veleta, the
foxtrot, tango, the 'Dashing White Sergeant': I played the old
tunes and new blood rose to them. John Clayton rose to the
occasion as no one else. He'd descended starrily into the baronial
hall in an immaculate three-piece suit with tight-buttoned
waistcoat, three-pointed handkerchief at the breast pocket and
frilly shirt-sleeves. His trousers were fashionably flared, his black
patent leathers shone upon the stair. His scrubbed rosy cheeks
had the refined chalkiness of a butterfly's wing. And he could
dance! He was the fastest, most rhythmic mover on the floor, a
ballroom sensation! This image was not wholly inconsistent
with my previous observation of the composer and my first
reaction was, as ever, one of rivalry, so that I considered whether
I mightn't learn after all how to dance, how to dress, and do the
thing with girls. But it had never occurred to me that the object
of my veneration, the genius-quickener of my inmost artistic
desires, was not only dapper but had a flagrant streak of
vulgarity. My own taint at the time was, I suppose, the opposite
condition: priggishness. I had developed a *noli me tangere* mien
abundantly evident at the dance – when I simply refused to go
through the necessary motions and make contact, however
glancing and polite, with the opposite sex; implicit in my
vaunted avant-garde preferences and my scoffing criticism of
anything from the romantic repertoire that was put before the
orchestra; and signified too, no doubt, by my trendy-fogey dress-
sense: sports jacket, beige cavalry twills (no jeans – not for a
long time yet), a ringed scarlet cravat, orange cotton shirt – such
was my repertory; oh, and that audacious mauve, red and
orange psychedelic tie, prefiguring the later manner of Bridget

Riley. It was a sartorial originality reflecting both a failed imitation of John Clayton's debonair genius and a failed attempt to resist my parents' taste in such matters. In me the priggishness endemic to adolescence, one of its chief strategies for coping with ignorance, was mixed up with a kind of superiority complex, the lurching self-certainty of frantic creative ambition – I don't know how these things fall out.

The informal concert at the end of the course was, meanwhile, the occasion of my first savourable taste of creative success. What a gratifying contrast to the night before! No longer an oddball at the dance, a prig, a wallflower, I took centre stage, gave of my utmost, and made a positive impression albeit with a piece designed to be witty, allowed even to be silly, even a touch Shostakovichian! whose dissonant counterpoint and jagged gestures were specified as parodic, zany, not my real 'voice', supposing I had one. Staring beside John Clayton – who had willingly fallen in with my plan – at the Meccano music-stand bearing my neatly calligraphed Academy manuscript, and concentrating like mad, only faintly aware of the timbered room, the rows of canvas chairs, the audience's eyes, I had a sensation of arrival, of being in my element, a warm and tense and vertiginous element of being on show and having but a single chance to get things right. Though intensely experienced, the minutes of the performance were out of time, in the metaphysical not (I hope) musical sense of the word; and quickly forgotten once a wave of generous applause broke on us. I was terrifically obliged to John Clayton for playing the duet with me. He, though, had a greater triumph on the same programme with a movement from his horn sonata given by himself and the orchestra's gifted section leader, Tim Brown, and two of his piano polonaises. If it seemed outrageously old-fashioned for a young composer in the 1960s to be exploring

Chopin's hallowed genre, John's results sufficed to silence any critics – me, for instance. He played with his customary effortlessness and *soigné* gracefulness, lips faintly pursed in concentration, expression faintly seraphic. His small shapely hands, ivory upon ivory, wildly roved the keyboard. Exploiting, as I could not but feel, the instrument's full resources, his music dazzled me even as it crushingly confirmed just how good John Clayton was at the traditional skills of composition, at simply – complexly? – making the notes sound *right*. I might try to explore the piano's total resources in a piece, but it would doubtless prove a wilful, artificial exercise, with modish devices like plucking the strings or tapping the lid thrown in for sixties' good measure. It would not be this decisive, hypnotic musicality, this naturalness. Such thoughts assailed me as I listened, still irrationally hoping that the music could turn out to be by somebody else. As an encore he played a Beethoven rondo, resuming the mere pianist as opposed to the pianist-composer, our district's Chopin, to whom I was most reluctant to apply what I knew were Schumann's famous words, 'Off with your hats, gentlemen – a genius!' But John Clayton, as I say, did not conform to a Chopinesque image; had nothing sickly, touchy or alienated about him, betrayed none of that smouldering intensity unmistakable in a photograph I'd come across of Chopin taken just before his death. John was the picture of roseate health, the good son happy in the bosom of parental adoration, the child prodigy who fits his environment comfortably and is fulfilled by excessive gifts which might derange another temperament. Mendelssohn, the calm, the prosperous, enfolded within a happy and remarkable family life, able to make everything he undertook an instant and exceptional success, was, after all, the apt analogy. What Forrester annoyingly blurted out in our music lesson had truth . . .

97

Max the Mighty

The creative example of Peter Maxwell Davies also fired my teenage years.

It was rumoured that during his student years at Manchester University and the Royal Manchester College of Music he'd done a stint of teaching practice at our grammar school, and I sought repeatedly, never quite successfully, to verify this. It seemed about as likely that Schubert or Britten should have schoolmastered there, though we were accustomed to following in the steps of arguable geniuses such as the painter Harold Riley or the actor Albert Finney, ex-students whose names had turned into prizes. Nobody remembered or had much heard of Maxwell Davies except for the senior history master, who was keen on music and took me aside one excited morning to break the news of Stravinsky's passing. He could recall the youthful figure of the composer, dark, intense, on the school premises but produced no details and was vague enough to leave me still in doubt of the thing. It was certainly the case, however, that the composer had lived as a boy near my own home. From Weaste the Davies family had apparently moved to Swinton and I was eventually able to locate the very road: a cul-de-sac of ordinary semis close to Swinton Fields, the last address in the world from which one would imagine the eruption of such a talent, such a dark insatiable imagination. But imagination is the word. External circumstances are evidently indifferent; the more dismal the better, from the imagination's point of view. For myself I was profoundly impressed by that very dismalness, by the way in which the extreme normality of our area and my upbringing was transformed and sanctioned by the known former presence of genius. Along these weary pavements genius, too, had plodded; within these grocer's and newsagents' shops

it had brushed its wing. I had – and have – an attraction to
normality in itself: the quiet undisturbance of afternoons, when
the world passes for running very smoothly indeed, whatever
atrocities may be being committed in that dark continent of
'elsewhere' – which, true, it is the business of genius to imagine,
as Davies's genius has always been willing and able to – but
whose real existence one can also, at ten past three with, say, a
light drizzle falling and the intermittent hum of wood-sawing
borne on the breeze, presume to doubt. 'Maxwell Davies and
Normality': fine theme for a learned article! Yet he bussed back
and forth to Leigh Grammar School, and back and forth as a
university student to town, in rain and shine, and again rain, as
averagely as you could want, all the while cooking up great
schemes for pieces of music, plotting his acquisition of creative
fiefdoms. And it all came absurdly true: the dream of success
was so abundantly realized that before he had turned forty I at
sixteen was devoutly bussing to Swinton Public Library to
consult the bound volumes of his manuscripts and sketches, a
substantial and to my mind luminous archive. The thoughtful
librarian, knowing of my fervid enthusiasm, would ring me at
home when a new Davies score came in. With a glowing sense
of privilege I'd climb the stairs of the cuboid, recently completed Lancastrian Hall, scene of amateur productions of Gilbert
and Sullivan (in which I sometimes played second fiddle) as
well as housing the library, and ask an assistant in the local
history room to hand me the as yet unbound publication from
under the counter and unlock the glass cabinet doors behind
which the stern-looking bound tomes by Davies were stored.
I'd spread my cache of codices on one of the large tables where
some elderly fellow might be reading the papers or an actual
local historian be at work, and catch that not quite musty,
bookbindery library smell. Opening a volume or two, I'd get my

first glimpse of such amazing scores – beautiful large-format reproductions of the composer's manuscript – as *Eight Songs for a Mad King* or *Revelation and Fall*, and find myself so overcome with stimulus that I'd have to go to the window and calm myself, vacantly gazing up Station Road (where L.S. Lowry had lived) or across the busy Chorley Road at the gabled church of St Peter.

Then, with a deep breath, I'd return to a proper study of the stuff. Exhaustively fascinated by the handwriting, the notation, the formal structures – or at least their layout on the page – I'd be consciously as well as unconsciously gleaning an abundance of ideas for projects of my own. The score of *Revelation and Fall*, a setting for soprano and sixteen players of a prose-poem by Trakl, was a marvel of formal sophistication and spidery notation. Never had I encountered such metrical intricacy: the parts were often in several (even actually seven!) metres at once or, there again, they might be in none, allowing the players freedom to determine their own precise rhythms. Ambitious, indeed reckless, was the use of medieval composition techniques, but, as I could hardly fail to recognize, they flourished here in a unique stylistic alliance with neo-expressionism, for the exaggerated vibrato so frequently called for from the violins (denoted by a widening squiggle like the twirling of one of Tristram Shandy's canes) evokes Viennese schmaltz, and Schoenberg's *Sprechgesang* exerts a large influence on the vocal part, which also involves outright screaming. At the climax, the soloist – who is supposed to be dressed as a Scarlet Nun – seizes a loudhailer and shrieks to an accompaniment that not only promised to sound a bit like (doubtless better than) the stabbing scene in Hitchcock's *Psycho*, but, in the calligraphic form of Davies's dotted verticals showing the rhythmic alignment of the frantically spluttering or glissandoing wind and violin parts, actually *looked* like water dripping finely down a transparent shower curtain.

Each page of the score – a *Shriek* of Edvard Munch's on its front cover – seemed as I turned it to be electrically alive with detail. Leafing through the big score of *Eight Songs for a Mad King* was no less catalytic an experience for me. I couldn't very well copy the uniquely mannerist notation by which an antique birdcage – for the birds that mad George III is trying to sing – is actually delineated in vertical, curving and horizontal music staffs (the notes strewn across them resembling twitterers). But I could have a good go at the opening crash, a delicious musical image (arm's length piano clusters, shrilling railway whistle, clamorous side-drum rolls, frenzied string and woodwind figures) of pure anarchy. Once again sheer genius had impressed itself upon me. Not only the musical discourse of *Eight Songs* but the text, sources, *mise-en-scène*, allusions, calligraphy, the intellectual *manners* of the composition and even the smell of the published score intrigued me and stuck with me insensibly. The work was the latest thing imaginable. I proudly played the record to friends, hoping to stagger them with that opening and tease them with the parodies of a Victorian hymn and 1930s foxtrots that come later.

From Salford Central Mission, where Maxwell Davies as a youngster had his first experience of music-theatre – an amateur production of *The Gondoliers* – to the Royal Opera House where his opera *Taverner* was due to be staged; from Weaste, where he was born, to the stars! The career was daunting and compulsively interesting. I was avid for newspaper and magazine articles about him and they were plentiful. I built up a picture of him as a restless, impassioned, solitary (I had no knowledge of his private life) but highly articulate figure, dwelling in a dark-hued, mysterious London flat stacked with medieval furniture and devoid of any such home comforts as a television. Here he produced work after work: *Leopardi Fragments*, *Second Fantasia on an 'In Nomine' of John Taverner*, *Missa Super l'Homme Armé*, *St Thomas Wake*, *Worldes Blis* . . . You could never keep up, his fiery imagination was at its height.

I had persuaded some members of the youth orchestra to form an ensemble in emulation of the Fires of London, the group which performed and recorded Davies's work. 'The Embers of Salford', David Forrester dubbed us, and for our inaugural concert at St Philip's Church in Encombe Place I chose the pair of instrumental sonatas from O *Magnum Mysterium*, one of the works for young people which Davies had written as a music master at Cirencester Grammar School. My new trio or *Triple Sonata* (as I decided to call it) for horn, clarinet and piano was going to be at the centre of a grandly theatrical and symmetrical programme, with solo pieces by me for clarinet and horn as 'off-stage' prologue and epilogue. The interval would overlap with the single non-twentieth-century item, a Frescobaldi suite for organ, to be rendered by an Oxford organ scholar-elect.

According to the scenario, I as conductor (John Clayton had never, as far as I knew, conducted!) was to launch the first Davies piece the instant the Frescobaldi had done, thus ensuring an arresting continuity; but I misjudged the length of the work and rose from my pew far too early, finding myself obliged to stand with useless baton at the lectern as though delivering a wordless sermon to the little band. I've borne a grudge against Frescobaldi ever since. But everything else went reasonably well. My solo pieces, modish *mobiles*, exclamatory and histrionic, were probably too ambitiously notated and easily composed, but resounding at the extremes of the building they made a dramatic impact. The *Triple Sonata* was brought off by a miracle of audacity and brinkmanship. My tense but vigorous endeavours at the keyboard come back to me, as does the atmosphere of group concentration and reckless shared adventure that wrapped us round as we negotiated the fierce textural and metrical complexities which, like the work's tightly interlocked sectional structure, were distinctly derived from *Revelation and Fall*; as we launched into the prescribed passages of free rhythm which also connected with Davies's music, not least the O *Magnum Mysterium* school sonatas; and generally rode roughshod over our errors: my own fingerslips, I know, were legion. The Davies pieces, pointillist, partly extemporized commentaries on a plainsong, were lively, all too lively, from an improvising percussion point of view. During the interval in the balcony where coffee was being served, Mr Baker surprised me with the volubility of his enthusiasm for us. The youth orchestra's precisely bearded, gaunt and intellectual percussion supervisor, Mr Cleeves, intending to write a review in the *Salford City Reporter*, was elaborately thrilled by the evening. I was pretty thrilled myself.

Most of us headed afterwards for a nearby pub. As we passed through the vestibule I glanced at our concert poster, a green foolscap sheet lettered in brown, designed and hand-printed by a grammar school art master. Immodestly I had let my own name – my three names, in fact, an imitation of the triple Peter Maxwell Davies name (though I could not compete with that pivotal, slightly sinister 'x') – be made equal in typographic rank with the established composers on our programme. Turning the corner outside I registered the church's curious architecture virtually for the first time, so preoccupied had I been during rehearsals not just with musical problems but with arranging the lighting, the heating, the interval coffee and such things. The oddly placed semicircular colonnade and round tower seemed to glow in the dark, as if with my own excitement.

Tucked into a corner of Bexley Square by the town hall, the Oxford was far too small for us, both physically and morally. With its fag-dangling men and women, their vowels as flat and hard as irons, it was hardly the sounding-board for some of my louder, newly warmed artistic pretensions.

'What I'm trying to do,' I was saying to someone who'd asked me about the state of modern music, 'is to make the atonal as flexible as possible, so that it can express affirmation not just anguish, Bergian astringency, you know what I mean?'

'Want another pint?' Forrester interrupted me.

'You reckon it went off all right then?' Tim Brown was grinning at one of the percussionists. 'Pity about the split note at the end of the *mobile*.'

'And with certain kinds of piece,' I was saying, in answer to a different query, 'it's true that pitch doesn't have *absolute* supremacy. In my *mobiles*, for instance, exact pitches aren't the most important thing really. The interest is in the formal freedom, or should be . . .'

'You lads bin practisin' in t' band, a what?' a smiling old chap on a bar-stool wanted to know.

'That Frescobaldi thing went on a bit,' someone averred.

'We could have had a better audience,' Peter Mann was saying.

'Thiy've bin doin' a bit o' band practice,' the old fellow informed his yet more aged neighbour.

We hadn't, of course, been practising in the 'band', not this night, but on Thursday nights some of us did indeed attend the weekly rehearsals of the grown-up Salford Symphony Orchestra held a few yards away in the Education Office, a building whose ornamental, polished light-brown façade made a precipitous impact on the narrow, busy Chapel Street, where buses halted at a point from which someone on the upper deck could easily glimpse Mr Baker pacing his office or discern the sleek black hair of the handsome Director of Education himself, a Mr Lewes, erectly seated with his back to the window at his directorial desk.

Past these offices, up a wide, formally elegant staircase you climbed to a chamber running almost the breadth of the building, bare but for an upright piano, chairs and music stands, a resident pair of keyed kettledrums and a wooden box serving as podium. I usually managed to arrive late, for all that the bus-ride to the place was an easy one, and the amateur orchestra would have already flung itself on, say, Johannes Brahms. Syncopation was not my strong point; I'd no sooner spot where we were with Brahms's tricky accompaniments than lose my place anyhow. Mr Baker was the conductor here too (there was no escaping his beat) – urging us on, inspiring passion, getting us to dig deep or at any rate play some of the right notes.

Not only a less than ideally skilled band, the Salford Symphony was never a large enough one for the piece, whatever the piece might be. It was usual, even at concerts, to play harp parts on an upright piano, a fact I found mentioned years later by Maxwell Davies in an interview, surprised (and touched) to learn he'd had anything to do with the orchestra. But when an 'awkward' instrument like the saxophone for Prokofiev's *Lieutenant Kijé* suite was actually furnished, the benefits could be slender enough: I recall a performance – was it in Rochdale? – of that colourful score in which the first few notes of the saxophone obbligato were recognizable but the rest an excruciating slithery squawk. Children and professionals, including a percussionist from the Hallé, eked out the middle band of solid

Thursday regulars for the concerts, which were generally given in Salford Technical College and always full of surprises, the first surprise for us being the exact composition of the orchestra. Quite well-known soloists like Semprini or Martin Milner would be engaged and the single rehearsal with whomever it was on the afternoon of the concert was apt to be a droll and desperate affair, the soloist reduced to scowling in no time and doubtless mentally scanning his or her contract for last-minute escape clauses. Stubborn as a trade-union leader, our principal oboe would invariably hold out on the precise interpretative points dearest to the soloist's heart and thus waste everybody's time. This not yet middle-aged, reed-sucking gentleman, gangly as well as bolshy, had a curious idea of concert etiquette. During any rest of sizeable duration he was wont to take out his wallet and count his money. Afterwards in the retiring room he was sure to be the loudest, most disparaging commentator on the way the pieces had gone.

It was in truth a ragtag orchestra (ingenious variants of evening-dress being proposed by the men), yet its technical standard was nonetheless above my own. I struggled to keep up in faster movements and the more stratospheric violin positions. I picked up a good deal, if unwillingly, about the romantic repertoire during my time in the seconds (I never made the firsts), and my sense of rhythm started to improve. My membership of the orchestra coincided with my last year at school, quite an *annus mirabilis* of creativity for me, leading to my departure for Oxford where I'd secured a place to read Music. Following as ever in the footsteps of John Clayton, I'd travelled south to spend a day exploring the university before applying there. But whereas he hated the place – his genius shockingly proving to be of an exclusively *northern* quality, liable to shrivel on contact with an alien milieu (he went instead to a northern redbrick) – I adored what I found, assiduously identified with what I perceived as its tone, manner, decorum. One afternoon some months later, when school had finished, I was duly escorted by a master into the cool armorial room used by the governors for their meetings and set to defining with difficulty what Debussy's and Ravel's styles do and do not have in common. Next day I was back at my post staring into the November twilight and demonstrating such knowledge as I had recently speedily acquired of Palestrina's 'species counterpoint'. I felt tolerably satisfied with my performance in these written papers, but the aural tests I had to endure in the Music Faculty at Oxford, when summoned thither for interviews, were worryingly hard (I lacked John Clayton's facility). Still, I had a highly civilized interview with my potential music-history tutor, a suave consumer of Senior Service cigarettes, reserved in manner, with a sturdily Oxonian voice; and was bucked when the conversation took a turn that allowed me to expatiate on the music of Maxwell Davies.

I hardly dared open the fateful Faculty letter which came a few weeks later. The main point in my favour, it turned out, had been the scores I'd submitted – my sins of the ear were evidently judged venial. But I felt I had already passed far beyond the stage those compositions represented. My most recent efforts were bigger, bolder, clearer, much more confident, Mr Baker had said so. There was the cantata I'd written to words from T.S. Eliot's *The Rock* for performance at Bolton Parish Church, where our 'Salford Music Group' had repeated its St Philip's concert. Then there was a four-movement *Divertimento for Strings* with which I'd entered a composing competition held by a semi-professional ensemble based in Cheshire. Boldest of all, crazier by far than anything I'd previously attempted, there was *New Vantage Points* for horn and strings, intended for Tim Brown and the youth orchestra but proving too complex and obscure for them. My infatuation with Maxwell Davies's music had been temporarily superseded by a love-affair with Karlheinz Stockhausen's – this piece was accordingly devised in 'moment form', each page of looseleaf score an autonomous unit, constituted by its own distinctive, explosive use of time, its own constellation of ideas. Unity was not now to be a function of motivic, thematic or harmonic working, but rather of the music's gestic impact, the sheer 'presence' of each of its consecutive ingredients, its moments; though I sneaked in a certain amount of the conventional kinds of cross-reference. The novelty of the piece meant that to notate it I had to rule irregular groups of staves on thick blank paper with a five-pronged platinum music nib. Never had I scored such a calligraphic triumph, no matter what the musical worth! It languishes unperformed, a lump in the throat of my memory; but the idea behind the work – that of constantly seeing the same object (which could be Life itself) in a fresh light, the unsecond-guessable light of its 'moments' – has a perennial appeal for me. The *Divertimento* which I finished just after *New Vantage Points*, and a set of *Three Piano Pieces*, written shortly before, seem by comparison all the more conservative in form and idiom, the first closer to Shostakovich than Stockhausen. I could re-evaluate John Clayton's tastes now that he had gone.

Oh, it was the high noon of adolescence when anything seemed possible, though not much more could now perhaps be ventured or achieved without breaking the mould of that stage of life; as duly happened. Perhaps not all adolescents can become geniuses, but the power of imitation and aspiration inherent in their condition is sufficiently remarkable to tempt me with the notion that every juvenile delinquent could have been a Rimbaud, a Radiquet or a Lili Boulanger had she or he subscribed to a different fantasy. After the last youth orchestra concert of the academic year the Director of Education, Mr Lewes, delivered a speech with his winning, rather Melvyn Bragg-like charm to the audience of parents in which he declared his faith in me as 'a future composer of this country'. I throbbed with astonished pleasure in my seat, formerly John Clayton's, at the head of the violins, in my blue-striped orchestra tie and white school shirt, and coloured at the thought that I should ever be equal to these words, this challenge; but concluding from such a public certification that I must, at last, decidedly be a genius.

THREE

Words and Music

Yet within a week of arriving at university I had given up the music course and effectively renounced my composing career for ever.

Seated on the top deck of a jittery bus making its way from the far north of Oxford into the centre, I see myself, puzzling why I had just bothered to investigate the Archery Club, of all the societal offerings of the Freshers' Fair, when I had no interest in the sport; and puzzling more urgently what I was going to do about my feelings of dissatisfaction and inadequacy in the face of the Music Faculty's demands. A bull's eye I *hadn't* scored, after all; and suddenly I realized I was going to want to aim at a quite different target. My confidence in my musicianship, my ear, had shrunk on first exposure to the frost of Oxford's prowess and competitiveness. I could not perform the miracles of harmony and counterpoint that the congregation of scholars at the Holywell Street Faculty worked with a flick of the fingers, a twiddle of an organ stop. To my conscious surprise, but as I'd unconsciously surmised, I was out of my depth. I had made a wrong decision and was about to be entombed in it. Even if, as I thought, I could cope with the music-historical side of the degree course, and in a cerebral, paper-working way with the theoretical, I would be sunk by the practical side, my defective ear horribly shown up. In any case I wasn't sure I wanted to devote three years to the drynesses of musical history. I'd had enough of Frescobaldi without pursuing his dates and doings and general contribution to the Baroque in Manfred Bukofzer's dreary tome! I craved a more wide-ranging, vigorous education in the Humanities. It dawned on me that I wanted to study *life*, not abstractions, not dots. But if I refused to submit to a proper professional training, how could I feasibly or honestly pursue a career in composition? And what hope anyway was there for me as a composer without a more intuitive facility, a native reliability of ear? I didn't want to embark on a lifelong business of compensating for deficiencies, of making music in spite of limited talent, depending on will-power rather than talent; though I later turned up numerous cases of composers who seemed to have done precisely that. I now felt – it never bothered me before – that you had to be about as good at music as Johannes Brahms to presume to compose. You certainly had to master those poor calumniated disciplines harmony and counterpoint, 'h & c'.

I had a successful counter-interview with my so newly acquired but wholly sympathetic tutor, who consented to facilitate my transfer from Music Honours to Eng Lit, though college permission had also to be obtained for that, and this time flatteringly reached over the desk to me with his packet of Senior Service. Puffing on that sleek white strong thing as though on a pipe of peace, I bowed out of music. The college took me as a literary student – I had the necessary A-level grades – and I began the second week of this Michaelmas term by attending a lecture given in the modernist sprawl of the St Cross English Faculty on Browning's dramatic monologues. I was elated and eager to be initiated. The world of Victorian poetry I knew very little about but its strangeness and obscurity were bracing. I need only glance at the contents page of a Browning anthology – 'A Toccata of Galuppi's', 'Abt Vogler', 'Master Hugues of Saxe-Gotha' – to be flooded with sensations not only of heady discovery but of delicate, difficult apprehensiveness as of a voyager still poised on his home shore, though with suitcases packed, having a quick coffee in the harbour café, before plunging into the New.

The little Victorian literary knowledge I did have was of Gerard Manley Hopkins, who stood at the head of the *Faber Book of Modern Verse* and whose sonnet 'Felix Randal' I'd set for tenor and piano some eighteen months before: the first of only two songs I ever composed. The other was my latest project: a setting of Sylvia Plath's 'Ariel' for glittering high soprano and brilliant, cascading clarinet. I resolved to finish this piece and call it a compositional day. In my unbeautiful freshman's room in the most dilapidated wing of college – a student warren on an eccentric variety of floor-levels – I deployed my terminal musical dots, my last and already lost bid to plant an importunate gonfalon on the high ground of compositional genius. This was as deft a twelve-tone structure as I ever made, an expressionistic treatment with a predictably shrieking, register-vaulting clarinet cadenza, but also elegant, I thought; clipped, cogent, and definitely looking pretty on the page. I have never heard the little piece performed and can't tell whether it comes off or not; but a curious thing about composing it was, as I now realize, that I had small idea of what the poem was actually about and certainly none that it evoked and enacted a ride on horseback, 'Ariel' being the name of Plath's horse. I listened intensely to each word as I tried to fix it in my notation; and perhaps my very ignorance paradoxically enabled a more authentic setting, as if by a kind of unconscious symbiosis, such as I subsequently found Schoenberg believed in. It was, at any rate, appropriate that this farewell piece should be an encounter of music with words, for a conflict between the two realms, each with its vast benison, was seriously raging within my psyche. That sounds pretentious; yet I felt I was being torn apart by my uncertainties. I could not lightly accept the abandonment of composition and all that it meant to my ego, my lust for genius-glory, nor easily renounce the day-by-day, hour-by-hour pleasure that contemplation and planning of pieces had given me. At the same time I'd started to worry about and balk at the relentlessly abstract terms of this art, affording marvellous satisfactions of pure form at the price of supreme obliviousness to the actual details of living, the facts and appearances of the world. Rounding the corner from St Giles' into Broad Street with two musician friends who were spiritedly gossiping, I knew, that second week of term, that I hungered for means to record the things of my experience, the things that were happening to me – changing academic direction, careering indeed along Broad Street! – all the new things around me. My Sylvia Plath setting could not, I felt, further that ambition; though if I heard it played today I might be surprised to find the Oxford of that autumn mysteriously infused into its lattice-work of crotchets, quavers and twelve-tone manipulations, even if no one else could be expected to derive from the piece such a nostalgic *frisson*. In thrall to the abstract discourse of music, I would, I feared, lose out on the chance to respond to and mould the lumpier discourse of life. Music or words? Words or music? It was the first of a series of nearly impossible binary choices with which life would present me. I was revolted by the prospect of artistic amateurism – an amateur composer was even more risible and contemptible than an amateur writer. What could I do?

I tried writing a short story. I completed it, but it was a truncated little tale, hardly plotted enough to count as a tale; rather it was a lugubrious review of my daily routine and inertia, my difficulty getting up in the morning, my procrastination, my peeing, my longing for an artistic destiny, my trip with a college chum to a film society showing at the Pitt Rivers Museum, my awkwardness at a party which he took me to afterwards, my vomiting there and queasy return to base with the prospect of another heavenly student day. In attempted tone and domestic earthiness of detail, 'Anthony's Day' was sub-Joycean (I'd read bits of *Portrait of the Artist* and *Ulysses* together with scholarly books whose revelations of Joyce's complicated schemata appealed to my composer's sense of form) and infected a little by the manner of Sartre, on whose *Nausea* I was embarked. This book I came almost to regret having read at all at an age when life was easy enough to perceive as gloomy, harsh, random, without need of such a thankless existential hornbook. The stickiness of 'contingency' – each thought and act viscously adhering to those coming immediately before and after it, rather than focused by any 'central' and benevolent purpose – I knew only too well. Uprooted from Salford's dullness and normality, deprived of a minor local fame, I floated uncertainly through my Oxford days and homesick nights, wandering blankly across Port Meadow or in the University Parks on dark Sunday afternoons; scribbling memoranda in a pocket writing block to anchor myself with at least the occasional dry, stoic maxim and urge myself to constructive action with the rallying-cry of a *list*. These were the sort of lists that are never actually consulted, for the writing of them is their sole justification, and one tends to remember important tasks all too vividly and remorsefully in any case. Swirling about me in the Oxford twilight was a social and sexual life which excited me very much, solid evidence of which, when it confronted me at the rather few parties I attended (such as the one described in my vignette), so overwhelmed me that I could cope only by immediate recourse to the list. In the near future I hoped I would enter the bright social whirl – I pictured myself tucked away in a warm, well-lit college room triumphantly conversing with a band of our university celebrities – but in the meantime I was what I called 'decentralized'. *They* were altogether elsewhere; and I was standing chilly on the riverbank in the Parks gazing at the opposite shore, which seemed to figure an infinite Ahead. Sometimes the verses of Decentralization found their way on to my pad, and the image of myself as a poet could seize me with a numbing fury. I would race back to my room knowing I'd got it: the solution to all my existential conundrums! But once reposed there, I'd merely boil the old greeny kettle, drink tea, and go on despairing at the paralysis with which my creative life was now afflicted.

Wonderful poems were, however, being written around me. In the fortnightly student magazine *Isis* I came across verse which for all its misprints and crude typography sprang off the page with an electric impulse and hit my eye with a dazzle. These words were gloriously new in their quickness and sheen, their suave urgency, their litheness. It was as though John Clayton had resumed his poetry pen but acquired a sensational refinement of manner and an enlarged vocabulary, full of the discoveries of worlds. My own music articles – for I'd managed to push myself forward as a reviewer – appearing occasionally beside the poems of this Robert Greville seemed a very jejune affair. I was lucky, though, to have my modest entrée into the glamorous *Isis* milieu. Venturing down narrow steps, against whose brickwork rested a flurry of unpadlocked bicycles, into the basement office on Keble Road one Saturday morning – it was my second visit and I was at once timorous and braced against that feeling – I was in time to witness the breezy, sexy departure of the magazine's star feature-writer, destined to become one of the world's most powerful editors. To be sure, many of my fellow *Isis* contributors made good, not that I saw them really as fellows, I was too peripheral for that – a sort of country member, galumphing into the glitzy office in my muddy boots, hoping to secure an assignment and get out quick. I nerved myself for forays into the region of the fast set, and slunk back with relief into the ambience of cosy unambitious scepticism afforded by my college peers, to whom the names bandied in the 'Private Isis' social column were as tantalizingly familiar and remote as to myself. That glittering roster was the eternal 'other', *Zuleika Dobson* Oxford, with its unique power to unsettle young people already sufficiently unsettled by their transposition from the awkward provinces and chastened to realize that 'getting' to Oxford is rather more, after all, than a matter of passing exams. Oxford was a neutral ground of alienation from both what you were and what you had hoped to become; not so much a no man's land as *some* men's land – and some glamorous women's too. Whereas I used to pursue the notion of genius in order to stand apart from my contemporaries and environment and be 'different', now I was clawing at it in order to belong, get in.

Of the illustrious band of undergraduates serviced by the lively student press the name that was most commonly bruited and with the greatest awe was Robert Greville's. He had his bohemian place in the *beau monde* (no contradiction in terms where he was concerned), but it was his intellectual standing that made the greater impression on us, the fact that he seemed nearly exclusively to consort with dons and be accepted as their equal though he was only twenty. Indeed, it was rumoured that some dons had conceded that Robert Greville's reading was wider than their own. Calculating with rough estimates, we tried to puzzle out how on earth this was possible. He had a beautiful knack of blazing past you in the street or on the meadow path, a Scholar-Gipsy carrying a bundle of small volumes, his bright cravat and eye gleaming, his demeanour that of someone at once inwardly distracted and in an urgent hurry. He gave you to think he was both highly image-conscious and genuinely caught up in reverie. A sighting of Robert Greville in the Queen's Lane Coffee House or Brown's in the Covered Market, holding court or sweeping off to a seminar, one most likely closed to undergraduates; or in the King's Arms, where he might musingly rest at the bar, eye trained on the glass in front of him, before looking around and abruptly realizing this was a crude element and vanishing into the night – these were, if not too rare, always events. (Many years later I glimpsed him in Paris, streaming alongside the Luxembourg Gardens in just the same wise, books in his hand, a colourful thick scarf flowing behind him. But this was after he had reputedly endured, or was perhaps still suffering from, a long and serious illness.) One had the disconcerting thrill of apprehending higher intellectual worlds as a tangible possibility. In his Shelley-like incarnation of brilliance he seemed a being of a wholly separate order even as he quaffed his half a pint. Shelleyan he was not, though, in respect of his academic career. He did not take the road of illustrious expulsion but the fast lane to an exceptionally prestigious fellowship. One shuddered with envy and awe at his easy fateful achievements. There was no competing with this. Even to consider competition would have been presumptuous, now and for ever!

His characteristic interventions in seminars are bright among my Oxford memories. With sweetly ruthless charm he would infiltrate the discourse, raising it to his own high level of extempore articulateness – in those fresh, urgent, clipped, somehow *smiling* tones of his he could easily frame compendious beautiful sentences which were perfectly printable as uttered – and informing it with his personal moral passion. As a literary critic he was a Leavis of unwonted loquacity: all gifted fluency where the Cambridge doctor was qualification, hesitation, fussy dourness. Robert Greville's eloquence was an Oxford wonder and it typified the values of the place, which prized articulate speech above practically all else and readily inculcated in its progeny a furious desire to speak with honeyed tongue and command all situations verbally. Genius was, as ever, mastery. Robert Greville as a poet who enthralled audiences at his readings – when the richness of his verse effects, already palpable on the page, would be indefinably multiplied – no less than as a 'situationist' of the seminar, masterfully prevailed. There he glows, lethally participant in a St Cross discussion of *Paradise Lost*, authoritatively questioning the late Robert Donnington after a Wagner Society meeting at Balliol, backing up Peter Levi during a poetry reading at Corpus, provocative at the weekly forums on Marxist literary criticism convened by Lawrence Cunningham, a still young don whose academic achievement at Cambridge had been hardly less brilliant and precocious than Greville's, but who, for all his charismatic radicalism, could not lay claim to Robert Greville's *sprezzatura* and easy, bisexual glamour. Greville gave out that he was both a Marxist

and a Christian just as Cunningham professed himself to be;
but his contributions to a seminar about the compatibility of
these creeds had not, I learned, gone down well: their brilliance
smacked too much of eclecticism and intellectual dandyism for
the liking of the politically earnest graduate students who
dominated the class. These were indeed postgraduate seminars
and I was an interloper, always remaining silent, baffled, quiv-
ering with the excitement of intellectual revelations – who *were*
Lukács, Dilthey, Lucien Goldmann? – thronging the air. But I
seemed to be accepted by the group and made several friends,
including Larry himself. It turned out that he was a Salford boy
and had been educated at De La Salle College, the city's
Catholic grammar school – for me, the archetypally Catholic
institution ('of the room?' I had mused and queried throughout
boyhood); and during my second Christmas vacation, to the
great gratification of my vanity, we actually met for a drink in a
well-known, somewhat sleazy pub near Manchester Central
Station and rejoicing in the name of 'Tommy Ducks'. Sitting
over his pint at lunch-time beneath the famous Ducks' ceiling
pinned with hundreds of pairs of *knickers*, Larry wryly evoked
his family Christmas: kids, in-laws, everyone noisily crammed
into the suburban front room with the telly on, and himself
puffing on his pipe, calmly reading Goldmann, Dilthey, Lukács
in the midst of the commotion, or even writing – for his fluency
on the page no less than on the platform was legendary. It
occurred to me how distinctively northern he looked, with his
stocky squat physique and plastered down fringe, slightly curling
at each side, and large untidy nose: proletarian to Robert
Greville's aristocrat; a roundhead to a cavalier. The talk came
round to the latter. Larry said: 'It was obvious straight away
that his reading was far wider, far more European, you know,
than anybody else's, even the really bright ones.' I flinched as I

had done when David Forrester had made that reference to Mendelssohn. But this was a different world, a literary not a musical world. I explained my interest in Marxist literary criticism, glad of the chance to do so without the intimidation of the seminar. He was encouraging, even proselytizing. As we were leaving, a tousled policeman popped out of a private room, and Larry speculated on the origins of the Ducks' notoriety. 'Special rates, no doubt.' We smiled and said goodbye. The afternoon was clear and bitingly fresh, Central Library's dome shone in the sun, Oxford Road was going about its great and little business, and I didn't stroll round town, I waltzed – inspired by company above me, by urbane, intellectual conversation, and the ever-fresh possibilities of genius.

North and South

But those early Oxford vacations were more often intensely miserable – confusing, disorienting, deranging. One must always return to the parental home, it seems; and all that labour of self-emancipation, aspiring to be oneself, steeling of one's personality crumbles to nothing in the lonely parental sitting room where you find yourself suddenly unmoored from all you'd been connected with, however tenuously, in danger now – how perilous the danger seems at the time, the existential moment! – of mental collapse. There I am, sitting up late by the little cones of red, blue and green pastel-coloured light dangling from the Christmas tree, at once so cosy and so definitively alienated; for I knew this place of cosiness was the last place I should be – remembering my childhood, lost in a vertigo of dreadfully specific memory, of nameless longing.

I began to despise and appreciate the environment of my upbringing as never before. I'd always assumed the region was much like anyone else's – normal, decent, even idyllic; but I suddenly saw the bleak poetry in, for example, cooling towers or 'God's boots', as I'd heard them called. I felt the austerity of the industrial landscape in which we lived to be a rare form of beauty. I'd stroll by the slag-heaps of the Pendleton Fault, looking down at the Agecroft Colliery with sublime awe. Here, in the *material* process, from within this earth, I reflected, society is powered and reared up and enabled to grow in complexity until it reaches the 'superstructural' level – Larry Cunningham's class encouraged me to think in such terms – on which poetry is written. Sublime Wordsworth and cooling towers were parts of a unitary reality; my environment was not something to be ashamed of, but a route to the philosophical heart of things. I wrote a poem on the theme, 'Radiant Geology'. I later learned that our local artist-genius L.S. Lowry had had an epiphany of this kind, a sudden getting-the-point of the sprawl of mills, chimneys, pit-heads, slag-heaps, terraced houses and crooked streets, populous with pasty people under a pasty unyielding sky, all of which he had, like me, hitherto taken for granted, or perhaps, being a reluctant migrant from the posh district of Victoria Park, quietly loathed.

But my feeling of shame about Salford – a place-name probably then best known from the subtitle of a Penguin book called *The Classic Slum*, with Lowry's vertiginous chimney scene on the cover – nevertheless mounted. My ear was newly full of the grating sounds of that Manchester and Salford accent of which I'd heard rather little in Oxford. In the men's room of a pub near my home I was surprised by the unsparing roughness, the involuntary tone of bitter aggression, the sheer 'couldn't give a bluddy damn'-ness of the way folks talked here: *It were summut 'e said like. Yer what? Am tellin' yer! 'Ave yer gorrit yet?* Certain vowels, like the one in 'bluddy', terrified me. Hard remorseless consonants struck me like a slap or a 'fuk' on the face, and I would find myself wondering where on earth I was. Could this be my true even if native habitat? It was no more possible to identify with this thick, nasal, uncouth manner of speech than with the cruelly ludicrous manner of dress, the wide-necked, floral shirts and papery slack-fitting suits worn by the troop of semi-moustached young men on Saturday nights out. The verbal aggression – redoubled, I suppose, in my perception of it, and mostly, perhaps, nothing of the sort – was balanced and finally outweighed by a whining pathos some-times, to my astonishment, mistaken by southerners for cam-pery, a kind of cowering humility which seemed to affect everyone and everything: not just the intonations of speech and the hopeful lamentable dress, the desperate attempts to keep up to the mark of fashion, but the very objects with which countless front rooms were stuffed – the trinkets, vases, cheap framed pictures – which inevitably wore an air of apology, of glumly making-do. More than ever it was necessary, I thought, to struggle to define oneself by *genius*, to lift oneself thus out of the engulfing danger of abjection. I was horribly wedged 'between two worlds', to quote from stanzas by Matthew Arnold through which I'd ploughed for my first year exams. To all I held intellectually most dear, to my best aspirations, this environment answered with an imperturbable assurance of sordor, anarchy, utter frustration. But now that I no longer aspired to compose, what *did* I hold most dear? What form and function of genius were available to me, even as an ideal? Poetry? Short-story writing? Journalism! No; it was still music that spelled true genius for me. However much I might dream of writing novels, poems or even dramatic poems (I'd been reading Arnold's *Empedocles on Etna*), the musical thing was essentially always what I meant.

Back in Oxford, for my second year, I helped to re-establish the Contemporary Music Club – it was forever lapsing and starting up – and put one of my own pieces, the *mobile* for solo horn from the St Philip's concert, brazenly on the programme with which we announced our rebirth. If only my piece had gone with as much élan as our poster possessed! a mobile in its own right, which could be folded and cut in various ways to produce a three-dimensional shape, bearing my name above a dotted line along a corner. Alas, the horn solo sounded this time like nothing at all: one-dimensional, a deadening collection of nugatory spurts, blasts and held tones, a barely adorned twelve-tone row. I wriggled with shame in the green-room, and would not come out to take a bow. That was it! It would have to be writing words from now on, or nothing. That was it!

And yet, as the composer and Marxist revolutionary Cornelius Cardew remarked: 'Once you have written music – not just dreamed it but actually committed it to paper – and not great music by any means, you can never be the same again, even if you never write another note. Once you know what it is like to move in that sphere, you always want to return there.'

I tried, indeed, several years later, to journey back to what Cardew calls 'the land of composition'. I even, through incessantly talking to people about this attempt, got myself a commission. I was asked to put together a score – it would probably want to be light, parodic – for a short student ballet performance. I was still living in Oxford, toying with a moribund postgraduate thesis like a cat with a sparrow, and soon, as it proved, to leave for London and the BBC. In my dusty bedsit near the Iffley Road I once more spread manuscript paper in front of me and started seriously to think about notes. But the bravado of adolescence was spent. I couldn't sustain even a page of proper, or for that matter inspirationally phoney, composition. I was panic-stricken. I appreciated that I was caught in a vicious circle. Only by attaining foreknowledge of my true destiny as a composer could I recover the skill and *chutzpah* to compose. But only by knowing for certain that I had the skill to compose could I now embrace and act upon the idea that I had a vocation as a composer. The exclusive mental conditions were rotating cogwheels in my brain which never meshed to give me motion. Prostrated before my younger and creatively flowing self, I pulled out my manuscripts to teach myself how to do the things I once could do. The works I had preserved were respectable enough, containing at least the possibility of musical life. The tone-deaf, purely notey pieces I had long since thrown away; even my large second symphony, orchestrating which had occupied most of a summer holiday, me scratching at my thirty-six staves of an afternoon while mother did the ironing, had been dustbinned. I pored over my old harmonic progressions, contrapuntal devices, formal stratagems: surely they were deployed with a certain instinctive brio? But on the tedious card-table in my Oxford room, I could no longer command such technical resources. The new score did not even deserve to be called stillborn – it was nullity. The moment arrived when I *really* packed it in. Well past midnight, I had a thoroughly demoralized wander, crossed the black Thames at Iffley, and made my way to a silent terraced street in south Oxford. I dropped a craven note through the door of the house where my young patrons slept, and stole back to my digs. A guilty thing, I had disclaimed my genius. I could not psychologically afford any further, ruinous trips back into the country of composition. l knew I had to kill the tantalizing persistent desire to compose music stone dead.

FOUR

Corporation Man

What, though, had become of John Clayton's genius years, now, after its marvellous flowering? Though I had lost contact with him before he left his northern university, he remained in my mind as no less shining and sustaining an example of creativity than ever, a memory easily triggered by items in my reading, for instance Hazlitt's essay on his first acquaintance with poets, or Stefan Zweig's evocation in *The World of Yesterday* of his brilliant schoolboy contemporary Hofmansthal (I knew these comparisons were hyperbolic).

Some years further on – I was by now a moderately well-established radio producer – an invitation came to attend and perform in a reunion of our youth orchestra, which still existed. I hadn't touched a violin in all this time and no longer possessed one. But it chanced at the same time that a friend gave me the long-loan of her father's fiddle, part of a consignment of lumber just arrived in London from Kenya. As though it were indeed a piece of Africana, a native mask or statuette, I examined the wooden structure, indistinguishable in its shape and detailing and feel and smell from what had been as intimately familiar to me once as my clothes or spots. I grasped the proud seahorse of the scroll, drummed the belly with a knuckle, and fingered the rough insides of one of the pair of curving slits which have the appearance of a musical notation already inscribed on the instrument itself. I admired the ornate fretsawing of the bridge and felt an affinity with the jet-black pseudo-lacquerwork of the chin-rest. The strings were old-fashioned gut, except, of course, for the steel E; and there was nothing fancy about the tailpiece, just the usual E-string tuning screw. This I regretted, for I have never been nimble enough with tuning pegs to be sure I wouldn't creak up the strings to snapping-point. Perhaps my childhood instrument was simply inferior. I used to rely at any rate on all four screws of my pricey 'Pirastro' tailpiece – ah, the word brought back Mr Aspinall and his unvoiced *r*'s! But I managed to tune this instrument with surprising ease, picking at the strings as I did so, remarking the funny hollow sound they made. I tightened the nut of the bow and, finding a glazed lump of Hidersine Rosin in one of the velveteen pockets of the case where the spare strings lay in their crinkly envelopes, unsheathed it, and rubbed its furrow along the stretched white horsehair. As I lifted the brightgold shoulder-cloth out dropped the mute, a little detached letter *m*, black, curved and funereal as a gondola, or so I fancied. I disdained its use as I prepared to break my long silence.

Ugh! How unmagical the sound that filled my flat! How could I have become so rusty! Or forgotten how difficult it is to make this instrument sound sweet? The strings whined and groaned under my shaky touch, my ill-conditioned vibrato. I fatuously swept the bow across all the strings at once. I tried double-stopping, knocking off the G major opening chords of a Mozart concerto. Then I rummaged in the pile of music I retained at the base of my bookshelves for a piece to try and play properly. Mazas's *Special Studies* in the Augener Edition? No, couldn't face those. Bach's *Siciliano*? What about this, the *Concertino in ungarischer Weise* by O. Rieding which I used to be able to manage? Semi-nostalgically I scraped away. I could still get through it, but how inelegantly! Soon, with relief, I returned the fiddle to its coffin.

It wasn't therefore with much confidence in my ability even

to get by at the back of the second violins – of the orchestra I
formerly led! – that I took the Manchester train one summer's
afternoon. In my parents' garage I had an anxious practice
session, directing streams of wrong notes at the freezer and
those otiose blocks of stone, before proceeding to a reunion
disco in the function suite of the Eccles Liberal Club, an ugly,
flat-roofed building hidden from the new motorway. Here I met
some old, familiar, not very altered faces – my coevals and some
of the tutors, Mr Birt, for instance, still a tease; Mr Cleeves, still
intellectually bearded – and many a fresh unfamiliar one, whose
owners were the gleefully congregating new generation of the
orchestra, an organism of necessity reproducing itself often. I
envied these young people their brimming enthusiasm and good
fortune to be 'in possession', key players in what, as far as they
would be concerned, was life's drama, not ghostly revenants like
myself. Standing apart from the red-lit disco-area, I mostly
conversed with one or two others of the latter sort, whom I'd
kept up with in London anyway, Peter Mann, now deputy
obituaries editor, of all things, on a national newspaper, and for
whose infant recognition and appreciation of my budding genius
I still felt (it was not too much to say) an inner glow of gratitude
and embarrassment. But there was no sign of John Clayton, nor
of numerous others of his date, Frederick Solomon for instance,
nor of David Forrester. Apparently, the issuing of invitations
had been haphazard.

Next afternoon, a warm and amiable Saturday, we recon-
vened in the hall of the Maxwell Building at Salford University,
where some of us as schoolkids used to attend lunchtime
invitation concerts by the BBC Northern Symphony Orchestra.
We never quite qualified as an orchestra to perform here
ourselves. A notch-up on the past, then! But better not take
airs, for I quickly formed a counter-impression: we just weren't

very good. Perhaps we never were? Everything about this reunion and our orchestra was a bit shoddy and disorganized. I couldn't even find a part for myself and my small, eleven-year-old desk-partner to play from. 'Aren't there any left?' I asked him. He looked cherubically philosophical. 'Don't ask me. I'm not in charge.' In the event we had to play three-to-a-part, which was awkward and compounded my already considerable difficulties. For the first hour we scraped and blew at Suppé's *Pique Dame* overture under the direction of the youth orchestra's current conductor, a local youngish fellow called Eddie Chadwick, whose rather acute comments on our playing belied his ultra-relaxed manner. Just before the break Mr Baker entered at the far end of the hall. I recognized him almost at once. Smiling, calm as ever in a crumpled lounge-suit, he was greyer and older, only a touch shufflier, more facially rounded. What caught me out when I approached and chatted with him was the northernness of his accent. I remembered him above all for those soft alien intonations which impressed us from the beginning and had probably lent him some of his authority. He greeted me warmly, told me he had retired from the education authority some years past and was devoting his energies to writing. Not music, words – books; and not just books about music – though he had produced a cello method – but thrillers, one of which had won a prize in a local authors' competition.

'I saw the advert in the paper a month before the closing date and just sat down and wrote one. Didn't take me *that* long. I've knocked off a couple more. Can't stop writing them now!' He spoke matter-of-factly. 'I'm looking for a publisher. Perhaps you would know of somebody?'

I tried to come up with suggestions while thinking that this could only be another example of pure genius. I remembered how I had dashed off my *Divertimento for Strings* in response to a competition notice and, like Mr Baker, been placed if not won outrightly. Oddly enough, if I'd taken up the offer of a public rehearsal eventually forthcoming from the Cheshire orchestra which held the competition, it would have actually been to this Salford hall that I'd have apprehensively repaired to hear my new-fledged music. Mr Baker wondered whether I was still composing and I laughed off the idea, inwardly wincing at the awful new need for self-apology.

'Are you going to take part of the rehearsal?' I asked him, and he grinned.

'I'm going to have a go!'

So when we'd all had our cartons of coffee he borrowed a baton and took us through one of the old favourites, the *Love for Three Oranges* march, jaunty, satiric, bitter and now, alas, nostalgic. I found this difficult to deal with too, wasn't up to the fast high scale passages, though my little partner pretty well coped; perhaps the orchestra *had* improved? Both bow and violin alike threatened to fly from my hands and clatter on to the floor but I managed to keep in time or at least stop at the right moment. After the run-through a more diffident Mr Baker than I could recall attended to one or two details – greater shortness of attack needed here, insufficient quickness of rhythm there – but passed over numerous faults which were painfully apparent to me. Of course, he had always had to do so! Mediocrity had ever been our norm; though I do think we had the saving grace of a certain ambitious *stance*: we took our music-making seriously, even if (individual cases like Tim Brown apart) we were not very good. Still, I was saddened by the present evidence of our tackiness, our raggle-taggle ensemble, acid intonation, our riding roughshod over difficult detail. Why couldn't we have been better? Less pathetic? Our pathos was alarmingly of a piece with that of *Salford* – the embarrassing word, the city, the slum.

We broke off at five. I returned home to eat and change for the concert, returning nervously to the Maxwell Building in my dinner-jacket at seven. I talked in the green-room to one of our trumpeters, a school-friend who had made a career of bandsmanship. Like Mr Baker's, his accent took me aback, but this was a northernness so thick you could practically touch it. Certainly I could barely understand it, except in stock phrases such as 'like everything else', 'at the end of the day', 'you've got different priorities'. The linguistic at-odds-ness, impeding our genuine desire to be cordial, bothered me and made me start to think of him compassionately as a sort of victim of all too unchanged circumstances; or was it just that I was a class-traitor? But I had other things to worry about: resining my bow, checking for my mute, tuning up. No one looked particularly tense, least of all the youngsters; but I was. Filing on to the platform gave me a funny sensation. I hadn't done it for years and the elapse of those years was suddenly palpable to me; the poignant surprise of playing in an orchestra once again, one last time, was arresting. Our summer night's audience was modest – a scattering of parents and some very young children – but I wished for no greater exposure. Under three conductors we got through the short programme without overly distinguishing ourselves but garnering large measures of applause. Speeches followed, inevitably recalling me to the occasion of my previous participation in the orchestra when the late Director of Education spoke so handsomely. Players presently mingled with the audience; the air was full of giggles, politenesses, the vigorous gambits of conversations long ago abrupted, being resumed.

Outside, as we crossed to the car-park behind the old fire

station, the sky was still light, the air balmy. We drove in convoy to a pub on the East Lancashire Road where I chatted to a limber, spotty, blond viola player from Manchester Grammar School, not particularly proud possessor of eleven top-grade GCSEs and six A-levels, which was surely a vast achievement, even by comparison with what I recollected of John Clayton's exam successes. He revealed in a broad Salford accent that he'd been brought up in a Methodist work ethic and was not bound for the sunny heights of Oxbridge but for the polytechnic of Leeds, whose advantages for his technical subject he extolled. Later, in the starlit back garden of a house in Swinton belonging to Danny McLaughlin, now the orchestra's assistant conductor – he'd led the concert's rousing finale, *Finlandia* – a group of us sat in a circle as though around a punch-bowl (at any rate a dubious home-made lager), old friends and new; and I felt thoroughly uncomfortable. Unlike Peter Mann, who gave a convincing impression of merrily mucking in, I helplessly per- sisted in my ancient youth orchestra role of aloofness; an outsider, shy, holier-than-thou. But now I really *was* an outsider, adoptive southerner, exponent of long 'a's, and not an attitudin- izing aesthete. Far from it, I was turning into a solid corporation man. I warmed to the social theme only when we decamped past two o'clock to an Indian restaurant in Eccles, where it was possible to go on drinking alcohol, a luxury hardly available in London. Here I at last got round to inquiring after John Clayton. Someone said he had certainly returned to the area after university but appeared all the same to have vanished. Accord- ing to someone else he was making a living as a jazz pianist in a Manchester nightclub, oh, where his extemporizing talents must be coming in handy as he wielded a socially useful instrument.

Next day, the reunion weekend concluded with a buffet

lunch on the third floor of the Lancastrian Hall. Climbing the entrance steps of the civic building I noted how shabby it had become. Its pale concrete slabs, symbol of a rainy working day in Swinton, seemed starkly incongruous on a Sunday afternoon of high summer. Perhaps because I arrived late, when the party was in giddy swing, I had a forceful apprehension of the unity of past and present (and implied future). There was Mr Baker encircled by girls who were my contemporaries, returned in the fullness of womanhood, some of them at a peak of professional success, one hugely pregnant, along with far younger girls who had picked up a clarinet or fiddle barely yesterday, also tugging at his suit. Marge Wisbech was especially possessive of him. Once she had seemed the most sophisticated of our number, speaking with every word and gesture of social experience beyond us. But she had never been away and still she flirted with Mr Baker as though no one more eligible in the wide world. I chatted, laughed, flirted myself. Some of the brass-players were drunkenly cavorting. With one, slightly my junior, whom I hadn't seen in a decade, I had a wobbly banter about the art of playing the trombone and getting into the BBC. 'It's all right for some,' he was opining as the youth destined for Leeds, with two girls I did not recognize, came over to say hello. Peter Mann and a group of other London-transposed people were already setting off for Piccadilly station. I was happy to linger here for as much of the afternoon as possible. I wondered whether on the floor below us, in the public library, the Maxwell Davies archive was still intact. Was it still being added to now that the composer turned out score after score in his new post-classical, neo-symphonic style which perplexed me after the burning revelations of the earlier music? I doubted it; public libraries had altogether declined. But I would have loved to steal downstairs for a peek, certain that the sight of those bound volumes would freshly inflame my imagination with a passion for genius.

I refilled my glass with white wine from the table by the door and descended half a flight of stairs to a window through which I gazed a while in solitude at the squat width of Swinton's neo-classical town hall with its improbable campanile, at the familiar townscape and the plain of Lancashire glittering beyond.

FOUR

Story of a Vowel

For whatever we lose (like a you or a me)
it's always ourselves we find in the sea

– e.e. cummings

Hold your tongue.

– Shaw, Higgins to Liza in *Pygmalion*

a northern vowel there was which heard a tape recording reel to reel of itself and found itself ugly as that duckling which was really a swan dookling the vowel really said with chagrin and displeasure dook dook dookling it wouldn't do why not a prettier sound like the new boy's from down south dak dakling he says larst he says or larfter or landon or lave he says and he looks different too what is it makes him so interesting the northern vowel wondered

so the northern vowel practised in the bedroom saying the words saying batt battcher bakkingham palace butt (batt) not bak buk *book* saying patting-green butt not pat *put* and not after all battcher one of the vowel's english teachers took it aside saying say buhtcher buhtcher was all right in fact the teacher kindly said and the northern vowel blushed it *bluhshed* it was in lave the northern vowel's best friend was as hard and no-nonsensical as certain consonants *fuk fuk fuk it* and they went round together all the time butt the vowel was unenamoured of this sound the friend made he was insensitive and the vowel felt oppressed by his hard remarks and hemmed in by everything every sound and even the very bedroom walls seemed to be closing in

one day the new boy from down south was talking to the northern friend in the school corridor wittily and the northern vowel joined their conversation about matters sexual what does that word *contraceptive* mean asked the vowel having heard the word the new boy from down south giggled and whipped out a cigarette sauntering from the school and the northern vowel afraid to follow

nervously perhaps the vowel noted the new boy's slender eloquence in the school gym unlike the consonant's thoudding about and the new boy showed an interest in the vowel's interesting library books about etymology and ecology and orthography one luhnchtime on the gymnasium steps and the sun was shining that day

the vowel knew the new boy lived with his mother in the mysterious new flats sunk into the space of the old demolished mansion also a friend of the vowel's who played records of avant-garde mewsic lived here with his father the well-spoken professor

the new boy started a saturday job now in willshaw's bookshop in manchester and the northern vowel bought a set book there a novel by mrs gaskell and admired the new boy's denim outfit his svelte sounds the new boy and he were striking oop a friendship they talked about art and music stockhausen's latest album stravinsky's death i feel free sung by the cream the pink

floyd ginsberg carlos castaneda the gothic symphony the northern vowel was glowing

the northern vowel soon went back to the shop and the new
boy was pleased to see him but busy in the shop and the
northern vowel browsed the shelves until the new boy in his
shirtsleeves said he had just to sweep the floor and the two of
them went inside the broom cupboard stood in silence a
moment amid the brooms and shuvels and the new boy's top
shirt buttons undun the walls enclosed them tightly it's now or
never thought the northern vowel it was never

years passed and the friends lost touch the northern vowel
moved south the northern consonant also and the new boy
vanished altogether now the northern vowel turned slowly butt
surely into a suthern a *sahthern* vowel and not all that slowly
actually quite quickly turned into that swan and was doing this
thing and doing that thing and going here and there and one
day in london outside the famous bbc's broadcasting house
bumped into a schoolfriend in the recording industry and was
told of many things in goodly manchester vowels for instance of
the new boy's continuing life in the north of england

but the northern vowel that had turned now into the southern
vowel then mislaid the scrap of paper on which the new boy's
northern friend had scribbled some vowels and consonants and so
the new boy was lost forever the new boy's northern friend also

years passed and one day the vowel was outside the posh
harrod's department store when the new boy and the new boy's
wife and children appeared the vowel slipped quailing into the
store tried to summon oop nerve and there they were again the
vowel approached them fearful of being not recognized but the
new boy's greeting was effusive his appearance wasn't altered

much they exchanged their news and wondered what became of mutual friends like the northern consonant strangest thing of all the new boy sounded to the vowel a northerner now and the northern-southern vowel blushed it *blashed*

the new boy soon sent the vowel a marvellous letter from the midlands where he was living now would you believe it the neighbour my wife has been having tea with once a week is actually married to the northern consonant we never knew till now yes the northern-southern vowel was truly astounded

another marvellous svelte letter came and another saying the northern consonant did have progeny as did the new boy but the northern-southern vowel brought forth only a book then the new boy left his wife and his progeny sailing the far seas of scandinavia and was not heard of then for many years nor was the northern consonant though probably now midland-ized heard of for many years

then the vowel decided to return home to the north and started wandering to the old familiar places the now demolished bedroom the school grounds the bookshop's site where the broom cupboard had been and the vowel was discovering the linguistics of nostalgia and had a dream then of the new boy far in the frozen wastes and next day thought to see the new boy pass by briskly on the other side of the road

yes it was me the new boy wrote in a letter the first for years my mother passed away it was my last time up there it's all over now and the vowel once again astounded replied saying it's a strange and good thing to be dwelling up north again

and the vowel mutated over the years into a northern-southern-northern vowel while the hard consonant apparently grew softer

138

living with his family on a smallholding in a vowel-meadow so the new boy wrote and the new boy was not so new anymore but seemed to have lived in a hundred places and travelled a hundred seas his speech now worn to the bone when the vowel at larst declared its luve

the first the last luve the embarrassed impure vowel blurted into the old new boy's answering machine the world's closing in the vowel suggested it's now or never the vowel paused it held its tung and the tape ran on ah

'Everything But the
Kitchen Sink'

a memoir

The oddest thing about the family kitchen is that although practically every one of its furnishings, cupboards, fridge, oven and stove, dishwasher, clothes drier, etc., has been altered, superannuated, replaced since the time of my earliest recollections of the room, and the room itself been radically changed, twice extended, it seems to me to be exactly the same place as ever, with the same atmosphere, ethos, flavour, the same quality of affording inviolable sanctuary, a bulwark against anything in the world.

It is like a string quartet of which all the personnel has changed, perhaps several times, but it is still the XYZ Quartet, with that loved and trusted XYZ sound, seemingly impervious to the years. Yet in the kitchen case there *is* a survivor, a senior member outlasting all, and that is the proverbial, or rather, the intensely actual, kitchen sink. The Hotpoint Flatley drier, luxury of the 1960s scarcely required in our age of emancipated washing-machines, has long gone, although the curious word itself lingers in my mind as a mnemonic wisp from the days when I would reach my hand into the apparatus's gradually cooling interior and pull out pale warmed laths to serve as swords. *Flatley.*

But the sink sits on there, proud as an old grandmother, surrounded by the succeeding generations, and a fair lick of life in her yet (true, she has been moved *once*). We go to her for essentials, for water to drink and cleanse and cook with, for the cutlery, cloths, towels and brushes, pots, pans and pails which live behind the snap-clang under-sink cupboard door and inside the sticking drawers of the metal 'unit'.

This metaphor, however, is not only a touch cumbersome but quite wrong, for the sink is really male. What is more, it is a boy like me, it actually bears my Christian name on the red and black-bordered medallion affixed to the unit front. How many times as a youngster being rinsed of garden soil, plonked on a dining-room chair against the sink, have I not glanced idly at my given name and unconsciously assumed the whole world to be organized around the fact of me!

Pure chance, of course. But it has left me with a soft spot for metal sinks, especially when, like ours, they have a single swivelling nozzle through which hot and cold water flows alike. And if the unit should be fitted with drawers on the sort of recalcitrant runners that were such a liability of my childhood, I should be perfectly wafted back to a world of agreeable music emitted from the wireless, with a great afternoon silence lying ahead; and the floor would be tiled in monochrome; on the redbrick uncarpeted step up to the dining-room briefly I'd be squatting; and it would probably not be a string quartet on the wireless but 'Oh what a beautiful mornin'!' or Alan Price singing 'Simon Smith and the Amazing Dancing Bear'; and the kitchen would be much smaller of course than it is now, but really much bigger; and . . .

And my soft spot would be softer still!

Bikelady

We were semi-snickering schoolboys at the grammar school, and semi-serious, with musical interests among others, even some musical ambitions. We all learned instruments, the lessons being paid for unhesitatingly by the local authority in an age when provisions for education were generously forthcoming. We certainly had no sense of being privileged to receive our free instrumental tuition and in some, usually stringed, instances our free instruments too; though we were jolly glad to use the excuse of such lessons to get off games on many an occasion and, even more gratifying but necessary, to get off big things like the annual cross-country run, a whole agonizing afternoon of running round a vast area of municipal playing field, an event which conscripted the entire school and left the classrooms almost deserted, peaceful but for the intermittent scraping of fiddles, whinnying of clarinets.

I took both violin and flute lessons and had seen a diversity of peripatetic teachers come and go, several of them 'mad' in one way or another. At least we managed pretty reliably to find them so. 'Flowers was on typical form this morning,' my clarinettist chum Woodford would report. 'He managed to break not one but two reeds, and he can't count to save his life.' Poor Mr Flowers was a novice teacher and couldn't hope to live up to the schoolboy *savoir-faire* boasted by Woodford, especially in the clarinet department. I, however, was afflicted with a flute teacher, Mrs White, who seemed to have no oddities and infirmities at all, was a simple stickler for flute discipline and altogether humourless; quite unlike her predecessor, Miss Repton, who had been most suavely sympathetic and whose lessons consisted of urbane conversation about life and the arts at least as much as they were given over to fingerings, tonguings, and proper breath control. I've often noticed since that a relaxed and sympathetic figure – teacher, boss, colleague – tends to be replaced by his or her opposite type, the 'now we are going at long last to start doing it by the book' type: a sort of systole-and-diastole rule of existence. But be that as it may, I now got a new violin teacher who did not conform to any type, whose eccentricity was limitless and unique.

Miss Hetty Rowe sailed into my life early in my fifth-form year, taking over from glamorous, super-cool Miss Hobson, who had suddenly taken a better job across the Pennines. I had felt a natural kinship with Miss Hobson, if only averagely impressed with her musical insights, and was rather appalled at the prospect of Miss Rowe. I was confident of getting someone like Mrs White, bloodless and severe; but far from it. When I say sailed, that is a true expression in one respect – Miss Rowe was 'stately as a galleon', a lady of ample dimension – but quite misleading in a more literal sense. Miss Rowe zoomed into our lives on a bashed-about Honda 125 with a tatty violin case loosely roped to the seat on which she herself, bundled in protective leather, implausibly pivoted.

We only saw this spectacle by chance, Woodford and I, slouching along the school drive, proceeding from the east wing to the west for the second double-period one mid-morning. Miss Rowe unwittingly chose us to ask for help in finding the music room and its denizen Mr Blackford. 'It's back that way and up the first staircase and to the end of the corridor,' Woodford said. 'But if you're the new violin teacher, we're some of your new pupils. Well, actually my first instrument is clarinet . . .' But before he could explain further the motorbike juddered, snorted, and seemed to explode. Miss Rowe and her violin case were shaken to the ground. Not unduly flummoxed, her spectacles awry, a heap of blubber and leather, Miss Rowe was making a sorry début, and we laughed. 'Darn this machine!' she exclaimed. 'I've had no end of trouble with it.' She reminded me of the White Knight in *Through the Looking Glass*, rattling in armour, always falling off the horse that is too heavily decked with his own inventions. Helping to lift the disparaged vehicle, we noticed an array of Miss Rowe's 'inventions' stuffed into its panniers: a dog-eared paperback novel and music folios, a lunchpack and flask, a knob of violin resin, a pair of gymshoes, a school scarf (not ours) and, reasonably enough, an *A-Z* of Manchester. She was not from the area. She lived with her ailing mother, it transpired, in Garstang. The Honda had been tested by distances.

Mr Blackford, our music master, was an undemonstrative man and showed no surprise at the untoward appearance of Miss Rowe. Other masters, though, were not above making sly and humorous comments to us when we interrupted their lessons to go to hers. These took place in a French-windowed corner of the main hall at the grand piano used for school assembly. My flute lessons were conducted in the sealed balcony at the other end of the hall, so it was up there with assiduous, dull Mrs White, and down here with anarchic Miss Rowe, an hour of each per week. The difference between the sessions could not have been more marked. For a start, Miss Rowe would be quite likely to be guffawing when I arrived, even if there was no one else present. 'What have you got for me,' she'd genially inquire, and I'd produce some Mazas studies or maybe the O. Rieding *Concertino* from my cloggy briefcase and show her where I was up to as I extracted my school fiddle from its box and tightened and resined the bow. As I tuned the strings she would punch the relevant notes on the keyboard; her pianistic ability did not stretch a great deal farther than that. 'Did you hear that Britten concert on the radio?' she might ask, rather than beginning tuition proper; and we'd chat for quarter of an hour or more about *Les Illuminations* or the *Serenade for Tenor, Horn and Strings*, or whatever I might have just acquired on disc. She was always enthusiastic, knowledgeable, and flatteringly able to make me feel no less well-informed than herself and someone whose opinions were not without value. Then I'd set to sawing.

Her technical comments were astute – oblique, unasserted, swaddled in joking and giggles, but palpable pearls of wisdom at their best. She taught me how to improve my rhythm and how to do difficult leaps: 'Try to hear the note in your head first, then just slide with confidence and you'll be there!' It sounded mystical but it worked. Sometimes, rolling up her satin sleeves, she'd take my fiddle from me – she seldom removed hers from its case, only really when we were to play duets – and demonstrate a point. 'Don't try too hard to wobble,' she might say, referring to my impatient efforts to acquire a true vibrato, and inevitably provoking in me irreverent thoughts about the easily wobbling jelly of her bared arms. She'd execute the problem passage with a certain deftness but in a tone so lacking in real vibrato (particularly by comparison with Miss Hobson's sonorous brocade) that I thought it a sorry thing; indeed I never accepted that Miss Rowe could *really* play the violin. She was not the least bit abashed by her scrawny sound. Though far from insensitive she had an imperturbability that seemed able to withstand any amount of smirks and funny looks and rude remarks, as it doubtless had been mettled on plenty. She could seem very soft and even blushful, but she was equally convincing as a toughie; at other times she disconcertingly struck me as something like a large but beneficent spider. Not that she was remotely capable of drawing people into any web. What was most apparent about her was the quality of detachment. She scraped on fiddles, exploded motorcycles, and went her own sweet way.

She was perceptive and kind about the tentative attempts at composition to which my schoolboy (semi-) seriousness and ambition were driving me. We tried out some little duets and she usefully suggested inserting a rest here, deleting a note there, to thin the perfervid counterpoint: I saw at once what she meant. Her vigorous bright enthusiasm was in stark contrast to Mrs White's patronizing dismissal of my flute sonatina. *She* had responded merely by advising me to practise more thoroughly if I were to be ready for the Associated Board examination at the end of the year. Exams to Miss Rowe were small beer, the real thing was music. She let me know that she herself had composed in her teens and had wished to go on with it, but when her mother began to be ill there was no chance to think of anything else. It was as much as she could do to scrape a living – her pun – as a peripatetic.

Unlike the other peripatetics, she managed to avoid much entanglement with the local authority youth orchestras which met each Saturday morning at a dour secondary school in the heart of the city. She took a sectional now and then with the juniors – who found her all too hilarious – but never helped with the main orchestra; unlike Mrs White, who rather pushed herself forward. Miss Rowe was always the odd one out, her appearances were always erratic. There was never a feeling of certainty about my lesson time. For a variety of reasons, some to do with her mother, she would fail to turn up as expected.

On the other hand she was quite likely to arrive unexpected, under the false impression that an hour had been fixed, or merely in a scatty spirit of hopefulness. Woodford and I always knew from the motorbike if she was about. We watched its condition decline term by term until it finally had to be taken out of commission, and Miss Rowe was reduced to a predictably dilapidated pushbike and the train.

Vague Mr Blackford paid scant attention to my or Woodford's progress in our practical work and, uncoerced, I'd been lamentably neglectful of scales and arpeggios on both my instruments, through a certain cussedness as regards the flute, and an excess, perhaps, of stimulus as regards the violin. Woodford had by now abandoned violin tuition to concentrate on the clarinet with possibly professional intentions: I feared he would put me to shame when the results came out. The last lesson I had with Miss Rowe before the date of the violin exam was on a summer's afternoon, when the rest of the school was occupied with cricket and the assembly hall was being quietly prepared for Speech Day as we made our lively din in the piano corner. Even now she was not averse to my running through, however cumbersomely and purely for the fun of it, the first movement of Beethoven's first sonata, a piece I always associate with her. Ruefully we got round to some cramming, but my scales were rickety ladders and there was no disguising the fact. The day was too lovely for serious worry. We stepped through the open windows and rested a while on the steps of the grass bank. The crumpled chiffon scarf around Miss Rowe's thick white neck glistened attractively in the sun. She took my hand and confided to me that her mother had finally passed away.

I have never seen her since, nor heard of her. She pedalled out of my life that afternoon to the refrain of cricket, a bulky, generous-skirted figure, still, despite the summer heat, packed into her habitual leather jacket, though she no longer, of course, carried a helmet. I sat on the edge of the field at the front of the school watching her risibly recede and unconsciously, I suppose, relishing our collusion in music: so much better, I was sure, than the pursuit of cricket or cross-country running or any sports. I wasn't surprised when she didn't turn up for the next lesson, but was so when she missed the next two after that. Mr Blackford could produce no explanation, and Mrs White didn't deign to consider one. But a few weeks later, when the results of the exams were out (I had just passed both, but oh! done slightly better on flute than violin – Woodford of course had gained a distinction), I did receive a notecard from Miss Rowe, prettily illustrated with a bouquet of snowdrops and green leaves. It was written in green ink in a sloping, moderately messy (two deletions), not uncharacterful hand; addresssed from Garstang, Lancashire, and its simple but oddly exhilarating, oddly enfranchising message ran: 'Congratulations on your success in passing not only one examination but two, flute and violin. I hope you will continue to enjoy both. If you possibly can I would advise you to get access to a piano. Knowledge of the keyboard is always useful, and I regret not having learnt sooner. Also, some people find a piano a help to [xx] composition. With all best wishes [xx] for the future from Hester Rowe.'

And that was back in 1970.

A 'Height' Inventory

> I know the reader doesn't need to know all this, but I need to
> tell him.
>
> – Rousseau

I remember, I remember the fine pain of the dentist's needle,
poised above my reclined defenceless head, then plunging into
the existential instant, for a time the instant lasted, I remember
remembering, I was in the grip of all my experience, my most
recent experience – walking along the dead straight shopless
street to get here, with the segment of park in the shining
distance where I could not go, and each time I looked behind
me the street seemed terribly charged with its own presence, its
streetness – forgive me – and I thought, I *was* there, where that
mother and child are now, a few seconds ago back there, already
in history, elapse of time being always immediate, and now am
headed for the surrender to pain, the absolute present – yet it
became a pleasurable surrender to the past, as I started to think
of myself as that child, led along a vaguely familiar street, one
of many, never knowing quite where he is, but always bucked
by, at home in, the world, enjoying the novelty of each
afternoon outing, finding reality ever so entrancing, my pain-
resisting thoughts alighting on the long curving villagey main
road along which I was so regularly conducted by my mother,

doing the shopping, the Height, it was, and I suppose just about
is, called: for when its buildings were demolished – all but three
– it was found to command a remarkable view of Manchester
and the Pennines, it was a shock to me to find I was practically
a *rural* child – I had mountains! – none of this will be of any
importance, I know, to anyone: hanging on to that old sunshiny
normality by listing its stations, its icons, the shops, one after
another, so familiar and oh so individuated, Westwood Church
with its alleyway leading to the first shop, a confectioner's,
Binding's, in the recessed portion of the road that curved in the
Bolton direction, then Kipswear the outfitter's, Hulse's wallpaper shop, Pickford's and Evans's, then wooden hoardings
(behind which that Pennine view was lurking all along), Stott's
the popular but unfriendly greengrocer's with the disconnected
piece of rusty railing on the pavement in front, the tiny wool
shop of the Beehive (where one of the two elderly ladies who
served always did so in a heavy overcoat), Wheatley's with its
smell of sweet tobacco, Rhodes's the newsagent's, the Height
Pet Shop, Davies's the gentleman's and boy's outfitter's (awkward moments there as adolescence dawned), Parker's the
butcher's, Murray's the newsagent's (Mr Murray a breath of the
Highlands wafted down the Pennine corridor, Mrs Murray
known for her raw-nosed good cheer and fingerless gloves), the
brief open space of Peter Andrew's coal yard, an off-licence by
the cast-iron bus-stop, Johnson's immemorial ironmongery (two
shops in one with double frontage), the old Height Methodist
Church, Tinker's the chemist, Profitt's the TV shop, Jolley's
our particular grocer's, Massey's the bakers, the tatty Height
Post Office with its back-room of cheap toys, Fieldsend's the
travel agent, Rhodes's (or was it really, as I assumed, *Roads's*?)
the bakers, Johnson's the greengrocer's, Arthur Pugh the dec-
orator's, Parrish's the quality shoe shop (with its boy-high, boy-

intriguing measuring apparatus you put your foot into), the inferior, ill-arranged shoe shop close by it, then the big Co-Op furniture store, that newsagent's with the emphatically though indefinably alien – and hence to my childish apperception 'Catholic' – feel, that funny, cosy, womb-like little drapery shop (like the 'Wool and Water' illustration in *Alice*), whose name is quite beyond my reach, the illustrious, awe-inspiring toy shop, and crossing over and walking back, Brumby's the newsagent's (of whose fireworks club I was a member), two contrasting fish and chip shops, the Wellington Inn, Height Carpets, a plumbing shop, a posh little sweet shop on the corner of King Street governed by a brisk, gaudy, affected lady who ruled with a rod of iron, the Waggon and Horses (it survives), Krink's barber's shop, the butcher's, the Seymour Mead grocery, City Garage, Barclays Bank (another if beleaguered survivor), Reid's heavily stocked and stacked wool shop (never say the Height neglected knitters), another decorating shop, a terrace of three private houses, the medieval cubby-hole of a cobbler's, Mr Howard's Gift Shop, Davies's general store – none of this matters to anyone, I know – another TV shop, the ladies' branch of Krink's, Kidd's the nonpareil of northern fish and chip shops (whose coveted secret recipe died with the last owner), La Boutique, White's the freshest of florists with its cool conservatory of a back-room, Morton's sweet-shop and gloomy café (some took a glass of hot Vimto here), Timothy Whites' the old-fashioned chemist with its old-fashioned wall cabinets; and rounding the corner – ouch!, that drill touched a nerve! – Joplin's the solicitor's, the spacious Pram Shop with its rickety staircase to an ever-unknown first floor, a hat shop, a grocery, and Dickie Price the no-nonsense barber and rugby photograph exhibitor, finally, crossing Claremont Road and along a bit, in a reach of the Height by themselves, the Pack Horse pub and the hugely estimable hardware and wood shop aptly named Forrester's, whose service, sawing and storage rooms one behind the other all fragrant with clean-cut timber were my delight – it's disappeared from the face of the earth, too – I remember, I remember, but I forget, I forget! so much gone, and how can I provoke memory, I wonder? as Mr M.'s metal probe worries at my tooth, into filling the gaps that remain on both sides of my Height, mysterious loci, habitations whose restoration would suffuse me with joy and create a mental, almost physical freedom, the information's buried in my brain, I know, and I try to prompt a Eureka! by flashing mentally up and down the road, yet though I easily conjure up adjoining geography – the vanished Redmond Street, Brazil Street, Torrens Street, and quiet little Claremont Place – the missing façades on the Height itself elude me, recalcitrant as a needed word that seems to float in the air above you but won't come into focus, and the more you pursue it the dimmer it becomes, well, that seems to be it, as far as waves of the past washing over me today are concerned, I'm invited to rinse my numbed mouth from the beaker of thin pink fluid, I plant my feet on the ground again, bumble past the aspidistra and soon I'm back on the long, straight street which has rather lost its *quiddity* – forgive me – in the dental, the mnemonic interval, but I'm glad to be done, back in the hum of the present, and the London traffic surging by.

Claremont Place

an oxo cube

1. Quiet little Claremont Place. But it's not so quiet now, exposed to the view of roaring cars down Claremont Road. We all, I expect, know a little dear place, nothing at all to look at, which others don't know they don't know, where perhaps we wandered inadvertently in our childhood and the meaning was little enough at the time, just a favourable feeling in the flagstones, a sudden dazzle on a dustbin lid, a flash of yellow and red from a washing line, a something uncanny in the twist of the path, but it leads sheer into a summer's afternoon.
2. The secret of this place used to be firmly hidden behind Woods' our local butcher's, before they wiped the butcher's shop away. Gone, gone the experience of this friendly butcher's never to be seen or smelt again, extinct as an animal species – a rare butterfly glinting blade-like in the sun, no longer sustainable on these shores – and hasn't left a sawdust speck, a drop of honest blood behind; only an oxo cube of memory, glinting in its silver wrapper, and the brash new version of Claremont Place.   3. This tiny bit of geography, no more than a plot of weedy soil, a dilapidated bench, an obscure nameplate, was the little clearing at one end of a tight alluring alley which ran between the rear brick wall of the Torrens Street houses and the miscellaneous back-garden fences of Queen Street houses nearly to the Height village and its shops. How the giant Height

roadlights – terrible searchlights – glare in the night! all too luridly apparent even at this distance, fixtures of the heartless artery the village became.   4. A 'Shopping Giant' replaced the shops, trampled down poor cobbled Torrens Street, expunged it from the map, just a discernible few yards remaining – a blunt amputated segment, like a nearly frozen leg of lamb hacked off by Mr Woods' thick benign and bloody blade. Mr Woods! so difficult to distinguish in memory from ruddily good-hearted personae of a televisual childhood, Billy Cotton, Bill Grundy hosting the *Criss Cross Quiz*, even the Daddy Woodentop doll from Friday's *Watch with Mother*. I watched with mother Mr Woods, white-aproned at his undulating bench, chop joints.   5. He operates his business at a lost address perpetual in the aspic of memory. From the window-seat of his squeaky-clean but bloodied shop, the odd Paxo packet on a shelf, I do *not*, while mother is served, glance across the road at the often shuttered, always slovenly and poorly stocked grocer's on the corner of dingy Saxby Street, both street and shop essentially out of bounds. I glance at it from where I am standing now upon the new boundary of a Claremont Place denuded of its tucked-awayness, self-advertised as an urban green regeneration project.   6. And I note the neatly altered shop-windows of a private residence – nothing wrong with that; and how the building's character has wholly changed, though it physically survives. Everything can be changed, doubtless for the better; boundaries come and go; and mystery goes. But they can't quite take away the lie of the land, the actual contours, the curvature of the road, there's some consolation. But they can take away the road! There *are* drops of blood on the lingering kerb of Torrens Street, blood of a yelping vengeful nostalgia. Don't we all have a quiet little Claremont Place?

Parenthesis on Parks

I would like to remember every small park we visited . . . As time went on and the shadow of fool-made history vitiated even the exactitude of sundials, we moved more restlessly over Europe, and it seemed as if not we but those gardens and parks travelled along.

– Nabokov, *Speak, Memory*

Unaufhaltsam heben sich die Parke . . .

– Rilke, 'Die Parke, I'

ONE

I love to wander in a public park on quiet weekday afternoons when the world's at work, the kids are not yet dismissed from school. Parks are life's parentheses, park-gates the lunulae, within which you enter expansively if temporarily upon *yourself*, swimming however briefly in the full green opening space which has always looked the same, always known and favoured you; a realm which quietly, protectedly remains there after you close the parenthesis once more, passing through the park-gates soon back into the world of trains and traffic, telegrams (they're a bit *passé* now) and anger. Parks are life's leafy truces, interregnums, pauses for thought; life's instant mini-holidays, its little Venices where you wander round and round sifting, savouring, worrying at your past, worrying at your future, beginning at last to plan anew, as you find your tracks coming back to meet you and see your shadow rearing ahead, like a premonition of your life.

I love to see an unfamiliar park – but parks almost by definition are primally familiar – stretching out before me, lawny, rolling, crossed with avenues whose trees, let us say, are turning as autumn deepens by the minute, leaves already lending the avenues a patina of fading bronze at twilight. My heart skips a beat. Perhaps they really are the truest medium for living, the best metaphor for our being here? Life is not a walk across a field, runs the famous, too-often quoted Russian proverb; but perhaps it somehow is? Life may never have been an Elizabethan pastoral, but one of its timeless necessities is a stroll across a park. My life, at any rate, is chiefly parenthesis, not much thesis; more digression and reflection than firmness of purpose and fervour of action. When they do away with parks, I may stop procrastinating, so I mused on the tube-train home from a favourite park of mine, Ravenscourt in West London, one such autumnal afternoon.

The tiniest, tattiest parks, even an allotment, will do. Take Elm Park, a mere scrap of green dropped like litter high on Child's Hill behind a pub with a fine view of north-west London. It is on a split level, its lower area equipped with three graffito-ed iron benches and a few bins. Poplars, alders, syca-mores. Look and the park has vanished! But its little emanation has hit your being. After all, it too is a place apart, sacred in its green and modest quietude. But I was recently disturbed to read that a woman was nearly raped in the bushes here. Parks are not all they seem, but they may sometimes be precisely that, viz. easy cover for a wicked act.

'The most beautiful place in the suburb is Scapelands Park,

especially when the weather is wild and there is nobody about except the anglers. When the wind blows east and ruffles the water of the lake, driving the rain before it, the Egyptian geese rise with a squawk, and the rhododendron trees, shaken by the gusts, drip the raindrops from the blades of their green-black leaves. The empty park, in the winter rain, has a staunch and inviolate melancholy that is refreshing. For are not sometimes the brightness and busyness of suburbs, the common life and the chatter, the kiddy-cars on the pavements and the dogs, intolerable?'

Scapelands Park is Stevie Smith's fictional name for Grovelands Park, in her north London suburb of Palmer's Green. She often depicted this park, in stories, novels, essays, poems. In its most mundane way it was a spiritual locus for her. I went there, not knowing what I'd find nearly fifty years after she wrote that description. But I was immensely gladdened by the place. Beyond the high wall's impressive iron gates unfolded a pure green newness which seemed to contain all parks I'd ever known and restore me to my earliest perception of a park. Hardly anyone about – the park was due to close (it had taken me long to find it) – and the sky a heavy dull white, the light fast fading at a quarter-to-seven in late September, the atmosphere thickly hung with moisture. On the far side of a decently sized lake a surprisingly steep and forested ridge was growing more mysterious by the minute. I explored as quickly as I could, greedy for park sensations. In woods beside the lake a leaf-strewn soil path crossed by a half-hidden streamlet led back into anciently familiar, vegetable places, basic as the bottom of your childhood garden. The playing field gently rising to my left was a hallucinogenic green in the bare white gloaming, sublime in a blunt, importunate sort of way, pressing itself on my consciousness. Further on, I found the tennis courts and crowned bowling green lying in their silent desuetude. I stepped back to the sloping field and stood awhile glancing at the old pile of Grovelands House just outside the park boundary, and, more intently, at the row of trees edging the field, trees seeming at once utterly familiar and utterly unique, even as they became a mere smudge of darkness. I was getting a park's 'staunch inviolate melancholy'; but I could easily visualize the bustling Sundays of its summer season, the boating and promenading, the somersaults, prams and ice-creams. Turning towards the lake I caught a flock of geese – more likely Canadian than Egyptian, I fancied – skidding down one after the other along their watery landing-strip. And I exited. But the park lingered in my mind all next day, *weighed* on it in a positive and existential sense, disclosing more of its curious nameless meaning, grainy and kindly as the white-grey light under which it had lain outspread. It was an additional thing in my life.

But aren't all parks fundamentally the same, presenting the same experience, merging into each other, having like dogs and cats a generic soul?

As often as I can, I give myself such half-day or day trips in solitude and take myself off to my secret places. It could be somewhere local and easily accessible, such as the Barn Elms reservoir near Hammersmith Bridge, a refuge for anglers; or farther off – say, Rye Harbour with its extraordinary shingle beach and quasi-petrified vegetation. Or it could be not too far off but not too easy to find, as was the case with Maryon Park in Charlton, which I managed to locate one weekday morning in early summer. I'd learned that this was the location for the scenes of harlequinade and murder in Antonioni's film *Blow-Up*, that enchantingly complex evocation of 1960s London, an intellectual mystery story whose burden falls upon what may or may not be revealed by a photographer's enlargement of his work. But the mystery story for me became that of research into the recovery of my childhood past – my early parks and leafy niches and stirrings of consciousness. The park, having already been made by the film into a kind of *text*, was somehow more amenable to my nostalgic hermeneutics than most. In retracing the movements of the film's characters – the inquiring, blond young photographer and dark glamorous girlfriend of the murderee – on that leafily enclosed meadow, with the leisurely steps leading up to it and the view commanded from it of a playing field and tennis courts alongside which the mime troupe passes at the end, I am the more actively able to ponder and retrieve the elusive meaning for me of parks in general. There is more to *go on* than in other parks, the brute matter of Maryon having been mediated by Antonioni.

Re-entering the film, as it were, whose setting has been precisely preserved, dappled trees, tufty grass, winding wooden fence and all, I feel as if I'm re-entering my past, the 1960s of my childhood which *Blow-Up* evokes better than most films I know, down to such lovesome details as the Button A on the public phone and that Mister Softee ice-cream jingle faintly audible in the background at one point. The characters' voices retain a 1950s plumminess even as they essay the demotic cool of the new decade. There is something early and innocent about the beauty of the numerous lovely girls. The freshness of the period comes through even in the dope parties, the guitar-smashing at the Yardbirds' rock concert. It is all one with the freshness of my summer morning's adventure in search of this park.

The plateau-like meadow is far smaller than I imagined. Like most people who give any thought to the film, I assumed that the mystery took place on a reach of Hampstead Heath, which is one of few park-like spaces big and complex enough not to be

easily reducible to a mnemonic image, and thus able to reproduce the mysterious sense of a limitless and involuted expanse
one had on entering childhood parks; as though, yes, a blow-up
of them. As one gets older, one literally outgrows the mystery
of parks: one is too tall now, positioned at the wrong angle to
the earth, for surmising the full fantastication of parks, their
winding paths and secret glades – which pall. Yet in a little
glade below the Maryon plateau I surprised myself by recaptur-
ing exactly, and for as long as I remained immobile, gazing
there, a sensation of the sweet, inviting indescribable newness
of entering Light Oaks Park in Salford, circa 1959. Quite why
this should be, why this glade and not another, this afternoon
sunshine and not another day's, I cannot say. All I know is that
I needed to make no allowance for the different, less acute angle
of vision; that it seemed as though the world had come to meet
me.

The playing field, too, looked smaller than in the film. I
walked right round it, alongside the tennis courts, wandered up
and down the adjacent bosky slopes, and finally out past a tatty
refreshment kiosk closed for the duration, hoping to find beyond
the park gates that quaint terraced street on one of whose
corners was the antiques shop visited by Thomas, the film's
photographer-hero, before and after his session in the park that
fresh, so very early Saturday morning. There is no reason why
the street we see as cinematically connected to the park should
be actually so; and I searched in vain, thwarted by the illusion-
ism of Art. But some weeks later I was watching a video of the
film and realized from the appropriate panning shot that the
street *must* have been linked in reality to the park. In the early
autumn I returned there, on an afternoon so bright that I could
scarcely see to scrutinize the park, my text. This time I
approached from the Woolwich rather than Charlton side, and

so was already equipped with a set of fresh impressions. I probed hard for clues to my mystery, as though I were puzzled Thomas himself, come back to search for the body. Finally I found my solution. In front of the main north entrance, which formerly I'd ignored, I noticed four tall impressive trees like those making sort of natural park-gateposts in the film. They must be the same ones, but the pretty terraced street had completely disappeared! Gradually I realized it had been replaced by a heartless alley of concrete living boxes at the end of which I was standing. Across this little road stretched a barely discernible line of worn kerbstones, at right angles to the new kerb. I was gratified to spot them, yet the sensation was almost too poignant, as though the familiar landscape of one's child-hood has suddenly been reinstated, and oneself a ghost of the future flitting across it; but it evaporates again, leaving nothing but some ancient kerbstones behind. *Pace* the plot of *Blow-Up*, parks are the opposite of thrillers. There is only the mystery-story of Being. And how strange that photography and film really are able to restore the past, the dead, into being; not in the traditional manner of painted portraits and scenes, but in their apparent actuality! This simple enormous fact, unimagin-able to so many generations, must change the way we live, change the nature of death. But isn't too vivid a recreation of the past unbearable? Parks are better, parks endure and speak of enduring.

TWO

Two paths. They're speeding no one's business.
One, though, at times, when pensively alone,
lets you go on. You feel you've lost your bearing;

till suddenly you find you're once more sharing
the solitary round-plot with the stone
and once more reading on it: Baroness
Brite Sophie – and once more with your finger
outfeeling the dilapidated year. –
Why does the newness of this find still linger?

– Rilke, 'In a Foreign Park'

In the part of Salford where I grew up it was always either Light
Oaks Park or Oakwood Park, quite distinct in character though
separated by only a few hundred yards, and forming a fundamental dualism in my mind, my homely version of Proust's
archetypal choice between Swann's and the Guermantes ways.
Broadly, Light Oaks Park was feminine, maternal, Oakwood the
opposite. Along the curving paths of Light Oaks Park my
mother for a period of my early childhood conducted me home
from school, which gave this – or seems to give it in memory –
something of the character of a secret trysting place. How
minutely familar was that daily trudge! the huge cloven tree by
the Russell Road gates, the heave up the hill, the grove to one's
right, the path running through it to the children's swings, the
rough-stone (usually faulty) drinking fountain next to the park-
keeper's green shed on the corner before we turned left, to pass
alongside the playground of the outdoor school, turning sharp
right up a sandy path, exiting by the park-keeper's odd turreted
lodge-house, with its hen-run at the back, whence fowl
invariably strayed. The park had copious hidden corners and
niches, such as the umbrageous duck-pond, or the bandstand
encircled by a secret passage of privets. On the crest of a mound
stood a little four-square sports pavilion covered with graffiti
and verandahed on each side. Behind that was a row of tennis-
courts; below, a putting-green that would one day become a

stab at a rose garden; and, hard by, the park cafeteria on the ground floor of a pointed-roofed building, originally a farmhouse, which was and remains, though long demolished, sweetly mysterious to me.

This café was a world apart. You entered through twin sets of doors, the first leading into a well-windowed, glass-roofed patio where wrought-iron tables and wicker chairs were ranged; this turned ninety degrees at one end into a space filled with broken park lumber, woodpiles and spiders' webs. I loved creeping round here and peering through the dirty, spider-webbed pane at a suddenly *different* park, while hearing the voices of the two or three people round the corner, perhaps mothers and infants, eerily magnified by the acoustics of the patio. But my priority was buying a lollipop or ice-cream cornet or wafer. I'd go through the second, heavily carpentered, dull green set of doors and approach the wooden counter which extended the whole width of the café's spacious stone-floored interior. As usual: no one serving. I'd look round the room, cool and shadowy, high-ceilinged, bare but for a dusty Lyon's Maid poster on a peeling wall and a couple more tables and chairs which were virtually never used. Presently someone would be audible on the stairs and enter through the door behind the counter. Who were they who lived here and operated this tiny 'business' on such a spasmodic basis, its opening hours limited to the point of arbitrariness; whose plumes of chimney smoke could be viewed from all over the park; who seemed to have some affinity with the park-keepers and seemed different from us, Irish perhaps? It is a lady who appears and at my request silently lifts by its moulded lip one of the four rubbery hatch-lids on the fridge and reaches into the frore cavity for a Strawberry Mivvi, which she hands me with an elusive smile. They never ran to much in the way of snacks here, no toasted tea-cakes, not even toast. It was just cups of tea, Pepsi, and the Marshmallows or Wagon Wheels displayed in their cartons on the shelf behind the counter. Nothing was for show, in its way the café was a monument to post-war austerity. Whenever I visit a park café today, for instance the excellent facilities provided in Queen's Park or Clissold Park in north London, I am astonished to have a wide choice of sweetmeats, astonished that the place is open at all.

At the back of the café-house was a fenced yard where park tools were stored and leaves piled, then a dim little sloping copse – another self-contained world – and beyond that the circular enclosure of the children's swings and roundabouts. In front of the café was a triangular plot of roses and a sward on which a Punch and Judy show took place one marvellous day when the whole park turned into a fair. The park was always turning into a new place, its geography to a child's eye was wholly fluid, for all that it was so deeply familiar. Each boyhood sortie, with its new compulsive purpose – duckpond surveying, soil sampling, birdwatching (hopeless tasks all!) – showed the park in a different perspective. But any stroll in a park should be a bit like that; a reminder that we do not live in a straight line, but familiar things can seem very different according to where and how we are positioned. Stranded in Light Oaks by heavy rain on a dark autumnal afternoon many years later I found myself huddled on a bench – prolifically carved with lovers' initials – beneath one of the blunt verandahs of the sports pavilion, pressed close to a quartet of young Salford marrieds, and necessarily listening in on their conversations, their lives. It was warm and rich and fascinatingly ordinary. The putting-green lay there impassive under lines of rain, the hut used as a darts club by elderly gents looked particularly small and wet, the thick dark clouds were almost low enough to touch. I seemed to have lived, vicariously, so much when I at length ventured into the still firm drizzle that I no longer recognized the terrain. I had been transported to another country.

Light Oaks Park, which struck my half-conscious childhood apprehension as actually light in colour, a touch fawn, was a soft, yielding, intimate, self-enclosed landscape, more mental than physical in the end. Oakwood Park, though not without its secret niches and maternal associations, had a more expansive, public character. Its acreage was more open, half of it comprising a windy playing field on a shelf above the main road to Liverpool and affording on a clear day a shimmering view of the western plain of Lancashire: you can feel as though you're gazing out from shipdeck. Games were played with especial enthusiasm in this park. There was serious rugby and football in the muddy mulch of the big field; and tennis on the three shale courts of the demolished tennis-club which my father helped to run and where he often prevailed in summer tournaments – I would never have believed this dear tumbledown place could vanish so completely! There were our complex boy-scout field games and the childish athletics of egg-and-spoon or three-legged races on days of municipally organized summer sports; and, of course, one's private, often solitary childhood games amounting to an intimate park-cartography, every knoll and dell, each fortuitous 'island' of rocks and trees or tangled rhododendron cave taking its place on the map of secret fantasy.

Oakwood Park was not an erstwhile farm like Light Oaks (my great-aunt remembers being sent to buy eggs there) but, like most public parks, had originally been a private estate with a big house that still stands: the low, moderately large white washed building called Ingleside, now an old people's home, in my early childhood an alarming clinic where I was taken for injections. I recall the medical odour of the place, my terror of the needle, my hatred of the word *clinic*, the cold stone, the waiting, the white-coated nurse ... but the memory is also, benignly, to do with the smell of bottles of milk. Not many years after my round of inoculations, I went through a phase of cadging rides with our milkman on his float, which I thought a wonderful machine, gliding along so quietly and easily with such simple yet enticing controls. We would float of a crisp morning between the Oakwood Park gateposts, crunching the gravel path, to deliver milk to Ingleside, the early light crinkling and gleaming like a silver milk-top. The dew on the park was one with the condensation on the milk bottles in their cool metal crates. The building could be plainly observed from each side, unlike the more secluded café-house in Light Oaks Park, yet something eerie hung about it even under such freshening conditions, and not just because I'd had to have injections there. It seemed so bleak a dwelling, all by itself in the park, so desolate by night. I'd no concept, then, of the mansion set in its own grounds, no idea that the park only existed *because* of the solitary mansion. Abetted or hindered by me, the milkman would dump the crate of clinking bottles on the proper doorstep and out we'd come, electrically purring, from the park, rounding the corner into Delamere Avenue.

I readily think of two subsequent, contrasting exits through that gate. In the trough of land at the back of Ingleside a fair used to be held on a Saturday afternoon each summer for several consecutive years, and this, though not as ambitious as that unique Light Oaks fair, was preferable because a more reliable occurrence which I could hugely anticipate for weeks. Here I discovered what a coconut shy was, and a bran-tub: the whole fair seemed a giant bran-tub when the dry dust of the park's familiarity yielded such an unexpected string of delights. But the joy of it all was spoiled when, on one occasion, giddily returning home for tea, I tripped on a tree-root and fell face first into a heap of dog's dung. One Saturday evening some twenty or thirty summers later, I was approaching the same point – the actual gates had gone by now – as I ambled home for supper after a walk through the park as far as Swinton Town Hall and back, when I was impressed – literally felt the pressure on me, as of a firm handclasp – of the Genius Loci, the being of the place, my sense of dwelling within it infinitely. Mystical apprehensions can't be described, can't, by definition, be mediated. But it was as though I were seeing into the heart and to the end of things; and it was good, and I godlike, but as the flower, even the *turd*, underfoot are godlike. The experience was intense and intensely ordinary. Elated in the warm dusk, I practically stroked the Swinton Park Road houses as I passed them, suddenly felt sure I could write about them – *save* them – as they rose to greet me, pressed themselves on me, spoke to me.

But nostalgically revisiting these two parks started early! My childhood became a sacred text to me, for better or worse, practically before I was out of it, while indeed still 'writing' it!

Other parks in our locality were less charged for me with psychological significance: Buile Hill, Seedley, Chimney Pot, Heaton, Davyhulme, Peel. The last-named – a favourite Salford subject of L.S. Lowry – was one of the first public parks in the country, pompously opened by means of an aldermanic cortège in 1846 on the same day as Queen's Park in Harpurhey and Philip's Park in Bradford, the three of them held by the mayor to be 'all replete with whatever can delight the fresh and buoyant spirits of childhood and youth', and collectively enabled by a government grant of £3,000 which was greatly augmented by private subscription, including £1,000 from the prime minister, Sir Robert Peel. Imagine a time before these spaces and those of the standard parks of other cities were carved out of the solid dismal conurbation! The intended oasis of light, greenery and clear air in London's East End that is Victoria Park was completed four years later, in the expectation of the Registrar General of Births, Marriages and Deaths that it would 'diminish the annual deaths by several thousands and add several years to the lives of the entire population' in an area where the mortality rate was higher than that of the rest of London. Apart from their benefit to the soul, parks were valued for their lung-clarifying propensity, above all in the industrial north where, as one historian records, '*The Manchester Guardian* hoped that the provision of parks would be followed quickly by "the utmost possible extinction of the smoke nuisance".' The Victorian concept of a public park was altogether of a melioristic space, something qualitatively different from the feudal notion of common land or the eighteenth century's beloved pleasure gardens or the immemorial village green. Manchester Corporation, acquiring the extensive acreage of Heaton Park in 1903, carried into the twentieth century this concept of a municipal space crowded with amenities – tennis courts, football pitch, putting-green, golf-course, bowling green, children's playground, greenhouses, bandstand, fountains, refreshment room, boating lake, swimming pool, menagerie, refreshment room, sometimes – as at Heaton and Buile Hill too – a museum. Having been conceived by philanthropists – the Stockport-born inventor and industrialist Joseph Whitworth, whose name identifies a central Manchester park and gallery, left £500,000 when he died in 1887 to be spent on such civic benefits – this park ideal flourished in the new century under the aegis of 'municipal socialism'; though such socialism and the park ideal have alike been somewhat wilting of late. So many parks and park facilities have a decayed look these days. Long gone the time when people dressed up for a day in the park! Peel Park is a shrunken affair, having relinquished its Victoria Arch and statues, and not much more now than a grassy forecourt to the expanding Salford University; not even the Victorian bandstand which Lowry so frequently depicted survives, though the interest of the park is now all in the fact that Lowry *did* depict the place.

But there is no excuse for not keeping up parks. We need them as the antidote to our lives. Ninety-three per cent of our time, according to a recent article in *Time Out*, is spent indoors.

THREE

Happily, Queen's Park, London, is looking good. During last week's Indian summer I walked there in sunshine nearly every day. When I first got to know this park I disliked its brusque bare quadrilateral, its lack of nooks and curves and hidden corners, the fact that you can see all of it at a glance – a park should never be like that – and not nevertheless walk right around it, for there is no cross-path where the pitch-and-putt course has been fenced off, and you have to walk along Chevening Road, exiting from and re-entering the park, to complete a circuit. This definitely detracts from the leisurely park-poetry of the place: this closeness to a metalled road, being on the wrong side of railings, severance from the accommodation of leaf and grass. But I have come to forgive the park this folly; grown, indeed, to love it these late warm days. Midweek between two and three – the best and most peaceful hour – I entered from Montrose Avenue. So brilliantly sunny and crisp! The world utterly lit up. The sky infinitely blue. Autumn leaves danced on the level field like static electricity made visible and lent a light-brown colour. Leaf-shadow and sun-glint declared new

geographies of glade; new, but at once deeply familiar, paths
and contours opening up which I'd been a fool not to distinguish
before. It was becoming a brand-new park. Squirrels flung
themselves about in silly delirium, scampering inquisitively up
to me then letting themselves be blown back as though a puff
of dandelion seed. They revolved and peeled their shiny *objets
trouvés*, efficient as a jeweller inspecting a stone, sitting neatly
upright to do so, panting, their fluffy tails a neatly drawn S. The
latter seem almost transparent, as if the animals were physically
sick and dwindling – but they are live wires. (Once I did,
however, spot a sick squirrel perched motionless and pitiful,
high in a tree here, emitting a fearful screech every few
minutes.) Clustered berries on small trees were pungent redness
redefined. The bandstand glittered as if just re-painted. When I
re-entered the park from Chevening Road, I noticed a man in
the silent transfixedness of tai'chi, a living sculpture. Such light
and loveliness and wide space return one to a sense of original
well-being, which means one loves all Being: that of the trees
and buildings and leaves and grass and shiny conkers and of all
the people, the swarthy gum-chewing man who asked me the
way to Queen's Park College – perhaps a new and apprehensive
student? (but I couldn't help him); the old lady who enjoyed
the sight of the squirrel I was enticing with a nut and condemned the prolific breeding habits of the pigeons. 'They must
reproduce themselves back to back all day!' she said, or something like it. I repeatedly stopped to marvel. The bandstand,
elegant and Victorian as the one that is missing from Peel Park,
a gently conical canopy fringed with ornamental metalwork,
supported on eight slender metal posts, seemed to drip with
existence, unbelievably full of itself! In its yellow, green, brown
and orange trim, it was a perfected arrest of flag-waving, an
array of festive bunting solidified into three dimensions, or as

solid as a thing could be which trembled with light. I relished the *thock* of tennis on the nearby courts and, no less, the sound of electric mowing on the knolled pitch-and-putt green, whose great shaggy weeping-willows had been trimmed to resemble bison the size of brontosauruses.

The following Sunday afternoon, fresh and fine, I played in a game of pitch-and-putt here. Here was a marvellous method of closely experiencing a park, a way of strolling slowly enough to ensure an active and intimate contact with the land – the contour, clumps of grass, quiet deposits of leaves at the foot of trees. In a state of just sufficiently braced relaxation, as we ambled from hole to hole, I had a heightened and involuntary perception of the airy landscape and the season. A far cry from the previous Sunday afternoon, before the weather improved so dramatically, when I'd walked around Queen's Park in cold rain. I'd disdained my brolly and had to shelter in the doorway of the café, where I patiently watched the weather thwart my purposes. This was what it is like, I realized, to be in the harsh element one so loves to contemplate from the warmth of cosy indoors; this was being on *the other side of the window*, beleaguered, exposed, shivering. My thin damp summer jacket was no protection – it was I who had to protect *it*.

From whichever gate you enter Queen's Park you meet a tripartite notice board informing you that this park was dedicated to the public in 1887, since when it has been maintained by the Corporation of London, and subjoining the fine print of byelaws. The three parts point upwards as though directing us to a park in heaven. I was once bemused to see a similar entrance signpost to Epping Forest, and wondered what precisely it was that one was about to enter – merely an *extent*? But can an extent become an *event*? John Berger, in his essay 'Field' thinks so. A park is partly a field and a field is what? What defines a field – or a forest: the fence that bounds it or something more integral, more conceptual? Can one venture a back-formation of the metaphorical 'field' – field of study, field of vision – so that a green field may become itself a field of study, a more metaphorical object, a piece of music as much as a piece of land? I looked at a field on a sharp gradient, tilted 'like music on a music stand' (Berger), in the Lake District one cold December afternoon and thought about this. Do I mean a piece of classical music or a piece of jazz? The latter, fluid, improvis-atory, is perhaps more like an average field than the former, with its more determinate, segmented structure. Miles Davis rather than Mozart? I pondered the different senses of begin-ning/ending in space as opposed to in time, the difference between extent and event. Similarly gazing at a field, 'into the silence, which was also at times a roar, of my thoughts forever returning to myself to search there for an explanation of my life and its purpose', Berger was struck by

> the cackle of a hen from a nearby back garden, and at that moment that cackle, its distinct sharp-edged existence beneath a blue sky with white clouds, induced in me an intense awareness of freedom. The noise of the hen, which I could not even see, was an event (like a dog running or an artichoke flowering) in a field which until then had been awaiting a first event in order to become itself realizable. I knew that in that field I could listen to all sounds, all music.

For Berger a field doesn't serve only as a containment for events, but, as a literal and symbolic *ground* for them, it finally *is* an event; an event in the life of the beholder, deriving from the contemplation a peculiar visionary happiness. 'The field that you are standing before appears to have the same proportions as your own life.'

Perhaps. I had, at any rate, a sort of sub-Wordsworthian feeling of visionary desolation as I shivered in front of the bleak green of this wintry field, littered with lumps of sheep and cattle excrement, dotted with clumps of trees, too dead to respond to the sharp mountain breeze. Life is nothing more than a walk across a field; *being here* no more than a mildly aching existential dullness. And yet the experience will surely produce an after-glow in my mind. Out of the dull dung will not a memory arise, a set of memories, an awareness of a stage of life, something towards a vision of life, even a piece of writing? Writing and dung aren't so far apart. Think of that tersely astonishing entry in Dorothy Wordsworth's *Journal*.

> *Saturday* [27 March 1802]. A divine morning. At Breakfast Wm wrote part of an ode. Mr Olliff sent the dung and Wm went to work in the garden.

That was the *Immortality Ode*.

Back to north London, about which an American friend has just written me an enthusiastic letter: *But, oh, the green! And that's it, to inhale cool and damp, that's an English park, and the last time at Highbury I stood with C. in his doorway and we both gloried in the fresh air and freedom that the Highbury Fields sent our way.* Only yesterday I took a walk in Clissold Park, not far from there. Finding it was tricky, though I'd been here a year ago, on a less brilliant autumn afternoon, when I'd approached from the Stoke Newington side. This time I traipsed on a circuitous, nearly hopeless route from appalling Finsbury, where I got lost, and Highbury, whither I escaped from Finsbury station on the first bus. I plodded back along Northolme Road, through Kelross Passage, and then, victoriously, through the estate called Highbury Quadrant, which I knew was near my little El Dorado. In a novel I loved as a child, two boys search their neighbourhood for this place they've heard of called El Dorado, whose existence seemed at least as definite to me as that of the intriguing Esperanto language I'd heard about. To my sense today, the very ordinariness of an unfamiliar neighbourhood like this one can seem as impossibly strange and significant as El Dorado then. We spend our childhoods looking for El Dorado and the rest of our lives looking for our childhoods, their magical, ultra-ordinary footpaths and streets. We forever believe we'll step into a clearing – the sun needn't necessarily be shining – where the whole blessed life of *then* will still be going on and we'll be able to enter it, and know that we do so. Tra-la. No point in getting too mystical, like Thomas Traherne: 'Boys and girls tumbling in the street and playing were moving jewels. I knew not that they were born or should die. But all things abided eternally as they were in their proper places.'

Thus I entered the park this time from Green Lanes. The sweep of fine grass, the trees radiant at the zenith of their turning, when I saw them first through one of the gates transported and ravished me. The purest blue sky there ever was! And silence incarnate, so welcome after the upheaval of getting here, the human turmoil of the environs, the vacancy and lostness even on such a glorious day of the Blackstock Road (I think I have to re-learn London). I sauntered over to the crumbling mansion of the café, porched with its six crude fluted columns, where there was a great buzz of chatter and refeshment-taking: mothers and infants mainly, but a fair cross-section of the community, with even a grizzled hippy seated on a slope strumming his guitar. I walked back around the park, past the 'Clissold 1 O'Clock Club' – it was five o'clock – noting clouds that paradoxically seemed to make for clarity, and at the far edge of the big field a white-grained light which paradoxically appeared to be steaming *down*. I stood with my back to the duckpond and again admired the whole gently contoured, undulating spread of the park, each stately tree with a ring of leaves at its foot, the grass radiating its quiet greeny force, overlain by a mobile zig-zag of enormously long shadows, and the beautiful beige sharpness of Stoke Newington church's magnificent spire to the left: altogether a superb composition below the hazy blueness of the sky in which an autumnal half-moon has just manifested itself like a faint fixed puff of smoke, a fleecy wisp of cirrus. There was a light breeze, an authentic rustling of leaves. Inside one of the green park-shelters, schoolboys were smoking and smirking in a cabal. Against a tree-trunk farther off a bike was propped and its owner, a leather-jacketed youth, sat hunched upon the leaf-carpet, head in a book. The pure mint-green of the bike-frame was another nuance of the landscape composition, it did something for me. And I exited from the park ecstatic.

Am I not a park *sculptor*, in Richard Long's sense of the word; carving out routes through a mass of park material; drawing a generalized map of the park experience, though valuing it for its existential specificity; 'sculpting' parks simply by bearing witness to them? Strange choice of subject: parks!

FOUR

Glows across Manresa Park
The altar-fire that no god sees

– Paul Dehn, 'Bonfire'

Of course, walks in parks are not always continuous ecstasy. One often takes one precisely to soothe a troubled mind, unravel a knot of anxieties, seek natural consolation for grief. Bruce Chatwin in *The Songlines* writes about the emotional and spiritual therapy of walking, simply being on the move. Babies, he observes, will cease their squalling as soon as the pram is pushed again. Perambulation is an inherently reassuring, potentially creative state. The 'songlines' of the Aboriginal Australians are continental walks during which the very world is 'sung' into being. Chatwin quotes from a letter of Kierkegaard's. 'Every day I walk myself into a state of well-being and walk away from every illness; I have walked myself into my best thoughts, and I know of no thought so burdensome that one cannot walk away from it . . . Thus if one just keeps on walking, everything will be all right.' Chatwin acknowledged that he himself could only write his books while on the hoof. And many artists have needed the motion of walking to develop their ideas, for instance Wordsworth, muttering his solitary way across half the Lake District, greatly nonplussing the locals to whose opinion he was perfectly indifferent; Benjamin Britten, who took his daily composing walks in Suffolk, usually with a dog, and sometimes an understanding human companion prepared to remain silent at his side; or Peter Maxwell Davies, who literally paces out his compositions on the landscape of the Orkney island, Hoy, tramping from hilltop to valley and valley to hilltop inscribing the 'magic squares' which inform his pieces on the land itself, assigning a topographical feature to each stage of a work's modulation process, and retracing his steps if he decides that a modulation has not been smooth or logical enough. Thus he takes the strain of the compositional pressure in his very muscles and tendons, inhabiting his planned work, as it were, from the inside and outside at once; a sort of double perception comparable, perhaps, to the experience of remembering one's childhood self, a now primarily external human existence whom, uniquely, one is also able to know from the inside. And doubtless the best way to write an essay (or parenthesis) on parks is to stroll around one, meditating the content and form, and closing an epistemological circle as you go. For the walk through the park inevitably puts you on the inside of the essay that will describe being *inside* a park.

22 September: Had a vitalizing stroll around Kilburn Grange Park, at one side of Kilburn High Road, a park customarily emphasizing drabness, downness-on-one's-luck, populated by Irish winos glowering in their appointed corners – but not today!

4 November: Mild but Novemberish, quiet, wet, drear, damp leaves strewn about, Kilburn Grange much more itself in this guise than in high summer dress. Tang of fireworks. Parks as living calendars, reminding us how the seasons are *in* us, and making our other notions of change factitious.

9 November: Definitive November. Drizzly, cool, very dull. Nearly empty of folk. One woman, one dog; then two men chatting as they walk. Sycamores just keeping up the appearance of a golden, though dimmed, blaze; and soon the twilight extinguishes them. Peaceful enclave – for the park doesn't actually give on to the High Road. You circle round the big field once, twice. Each revolution changes your mentality. Each time you arrive at, say, a point near the dog-free zone, you are a slightly different person. The circling conduces to meditation: first you deal with immediate matters, things to do in the next few hours, days; then you manage to reach out to longer-term more philosophical or spiritual matters; finally (if you can) to spirituality itself. You are re-orienting yourself within your own life, but as you do so layers of self peel off, and you start to gain a sense of *other* lives, their palpable reality, yes.

And by means of parks you can orientate yourself anywhere.

What town or city is too remote or exotic not to offer some secluded plot of green in which you may wander assured of self-communion and feelings of recognition? I think of a little rectangular park – a park without a name – in Milan; or that elegant park of fountains and avenues on a hill in Brussels, where I fancied one of Rilke's solitary, letter-writing figures might flit; of Amsterdam's big brash Vondelpark and its more secretive Sarphati Park; of the classic poise of the Luxembourg Gardens in Paris, the rolling extravagance of Munich's English Gardens, the rich level spread and formal charms of London's Regent's Park, or the perfect provincial intimacy of Greenhead Park in Huddersfield. However varied in form or mood, parks put you readily in touch with urban values nearly universal, intuited already in babyhood when you were pushed in your pram to the local duckpond. What you find when you exit from the park in the new city cannot surely now be so very different from the world you've known of old. For the person lost in an unfamiliar city, or even in a familiar one, the parks await with their mysticism and reassurance.

Manresa Park, Chelsea: a name without a park. One afternoon I tried to locate it, but it simply *isn't*; has evidently been built over by the Chelsea College of Art. Chelsea Square, at the end of Manresa Road, must suffice. Here I peered through the railings at a row of unusually squat red roses and a scatter of crisp browned leaves, and was plunged deep into a dream dreamed long ago, suddenly so familiar.

Far from guaranteeing a continuous ecstasy, a walk of any length within or without a park, lacking a Brittenish or Maxwell Davies-like agenda – and what kind of walk is it, after all, with a composer's deadline affixed – is liable to take you down as well as up. You find that the creative energy easily gathering force at the outset, when the world slips back obligingly into one of pure possibility, can be dissipated by the time you are let us say three-quarters of the way, on the homeward leg. You are beset by flagging spirits, a sudden dry-throated hopelessness, a fatigue that is also a nagging existential irritation. Nothing seems right. The world is opaque again. You curse all work of your own hands. Now you are not so much on a 'walk' – that benign thing – as in a state of passive transition, merely waiting for a change of state. Certain locations epitomize this feeling for me: in London the trudge up Haverstock Hill between Belsize Park and Hampstead High Street; or that blank if brief stretch from West End Green to Fortune Green, which has you winding past indifferent low blocks of flats, and makes the achievement of the little green veritably a stroke of good fortune. Arbitrary enough examples of a feeling of arbitrariness. But you press on, and gradually the feeling passes, the mental nausea lifts, bodily robustness restores the spirits. You return home exhilarated just the same.

Even when accompanied on a walk, you are likely to undergo such alteration of moods. The mind's habitual conversation with itself, its wrestling with desire, forms a secret counterpoint to any actual conversation you may be holding. Have we, I wondered the other week, made inward progress since we entered (trespassing!) this private park near Winchmore Hill? For however short the elapse of time, both A. and I will emerge a different person. The groves' autumn brilliance, the ploughed field, the discomposed pheasants' loud kerfuffle will at once seem things of the past. Moods are traversed at more than a strolling pace. To have crossed the park is to have lived a life in little.

But that sinking feeling on a walk may be more prosaically attributed to what you actually find as you go. Returning to Ravenscourt Park after a couple of years, I hoped for a walk straight along an early autumnal avenue into the Sublime. But I had chosen too late an afternoon hour, almost 6 pm. The park was thoroughly given over to its civic uses, everyone in it had a practical purpose (whereas mine was inexpressibly unpractical): tennis players, runners, joggers, schoolchildren withdrawing themselves for a smoke, homosexuals loitering within eyeing distance of the public lavatory and silently foregathering in the enclosed garden. The playground was full of noisy kids; kids were catapulting at birds in the trees by the duckpond. Grey-suited businessmen, taking their small rations of daily air, walked briefcases home along a diagonal into the bosom of the middle-class. Dog-walkers were rife, and I wondered how many of them actually use the red boxes provided in a spirit both beneficent and authoritarian by the council for the animals' excrement and which give the modern park a curiously postal feel. No, I did not float. I felt anxious. The greensward unrolled handsomely before me, while the dusk began to turn people into looming anonymities, deepening the gold of fallen leaves; but I had not had my moment. The park seemed compromised, spoiled, not a bit Rilkean! The more bustlingly a park is used for its civic amenities, the less becomes its spiritual amenity, the vaguer one's sense of it as a fully enclosing space, an instrument of being, a gateway to a better world. The note of the afternoon turned out to be not sublimity, indeed, but low comedy. I noticed that what used to be the public pissoir, a gingerbread cottage in the middle of King Street, opposite the park gates, had been revamped into a pizzeria. Where once you pissed, you *pizza*.

Evidence of vandalism in parks is particularly distressing: a wound inflicted on the public by itself. Once, an afternoon at Christmas, I walked in Light Oaks Park to find that the park-keepers' wooden shed, the erstwhile darts club, fragant with elderly decades of pipe smoke, had been literally burnt to a cinder. I stood among the cinders on the concrete base and picked among the rubble. The charred page of a park-keeper's log-book had survived, uselessly preserving summer planting information scrawled in pithy memoranda. A vista had been opened towards the bare copse at the back of the playground, and thus had the vandals reconfigured the park's geography. Two small innocent boys on bicycles stopped to marvel at the site and rummage for spoils. An elderly lady stood by me, tut-tutting. Later on the same walk, I was even more startled and upset to discover a burnt-out car nosing out of the bushes beside the duckpond. Two more such cars dismayingly presented themselves to me in the course of the afternoon, one on a grass verge in Buile Hill Park, another perched on the raised level of my old school playing-field, overhanging the wall of the road which divided the boys' from the girls' grammar schools, an almost mythical intersection for me, recurring in my dreams. My ghosts throng thickly here, and I was all the more hurt and bewildered by what must have been going on the night before. Holiday youths on a drugged and drunken car-jacking spree. Parks bleeding.

And the same thing happened to the keeper's shed in Kilburn Grange Park. One day it, too, was reduced to its base and a few charred beams, an outflow of meagre contents, bits of paper, cans, torn magazines. Parks will be attacked at their most vulnerable, man-made point. Try burning down a holm-oak! Park-vandals are childish in the strict sense in which children will never let each other alone, must punish each other for their very being: merely because there are sanctuaries from the hurly-burly of life, hurly-burly must be visited upon them. If the parks are desecrated, if one is not protected here, where *can* one go for spiritual refuge without mournfully resorting to the cold stone of an unlocked church? Yet the idea that parks offer protection will be risible to many. Increasingly, parks are just where you *don't* go. Women and children especially don't go. The shady paths, winding around the park like a blood-circulation system, are camouflage for psychotics, rapists, murderers. Riddlesdown Common in Croydon, Grimaldi Park in Islington, the aforementioned Elm Park have become as perilous as Central Park, New York. It's not just the lost or eccentric, the flasher or the bag lady, or those sad souls maimed by life like Baudelaire's stoical penniless widows who are haunting the parks. It's the criminally insane, and their numbers are swelling. There are times when the parks seem irreversibly tainted, as wholly negative as they once appeared to Rilke:

> . . . in the distance the stone balustrades
> have closed the paths, as if with barricades.

> . . . as if it were accursed is each bird's call,
> and as if poisoned every nightingale.

> . . . a black
> swarm of gnats is buzzing all about,
> as if there, instantly! behind your back
> everything were destroyed and blotted out.

> – 'The Parks', VII

FIVE

Thumping along each road today are cars transformed by their drivers into raving discothèques. Drummers performing in Leicester Square nightly go berserk. Pursuing the life of sensual abandon legitimately enough, my Kilburn neighbour makes the walls heave horribly each afternoon at five. In an age of pervasive din, of social congestion, heartlessness and worse, what is it but parks that slenderly sustain our hopes for the tranquil life, for inwardness and havens of intenseness? More and more it seems that parks, with all their vulnerability to misuse, are all we've got – not parenthetical at all! Against the depredations of 'fool-made history', they hold out as conduits to our first and better world, giving us a sensation of self-recovery which is not fundamentally nostalgic and escapist because it is the present-ness of the *present* as much as that of the past which is rendered. Parks are havens also of reality. As I've suggested, the world is not wide enough to cut off access to one's deepest self through parks. In a park in Tokyo, gazing up at a giant red torii, I could be wandering again in Oakwood Park, crunching the Lancashire leaves. The melancholy quiet of the public gardens secreted at the Lido end of Venice – the city whose whole extent and being is a park for the soul – is a rainy afternoon in Light Oaks Park. Either way it is the actuality of my being that I am experiencing, and the sovereign nature of experience itself.

Irresistibly the parks arise . . .

Those *giardini* I lazily failed to locate on several visits to Venice, and couldn't quite credit their existence. The cramped islands seemed most unlikely to afford such an open space. I had found, easily enough, the summer-dusty scrap of public garden on the Molo, but could not believe that this was my goal. Eventually, on a dull wet afternoon late one autumn, I stumbled upon the free-standing portal of the *giardini* and triumphantly entered. In the seasonal light the vague bunched outlines of the trees were at once ominous and cosy. Broken and glaring statuary – a crumbling headless Flora, a lion with St Mark – disarmed me (I was the only person about) at every turn. The leaves dripped sadly, and I had the curious impression of being sucked into the very soil. I felt I could hear the earth weeping, a very little. Ghosts of the summer festivities had a flickering presence, while at the same time everything seemed profoundly *normal*. The national pavilions of the Biennale looked wanly derelict, irretrievably out of bounds. Trying in vain to attract the attention of even the less timid of the congregated cats for whom a part of the park is their citadel, I strolled on, receiving, at least, a stone nod from the surprising huge figure of Neptune, recumbent on the sea-steps into the lagoon; and crossed a canal bridge into the peaceful, untouristed expanse of Parco delle Rimembranze, where a few boys were playing quiet football under the immense canopy of trees. The illuminated shop-front of a café on the Viale Quattro Novembre – so beautifully named – was a welcome. At a table by the window, I toyed with a cappuccino and a glass of *prosecco* and pondered on my previous visits to Venice, previous emotional stocktakings, savouring a delicious solitude.

FIVE

Chastity

final monologue of an old painter

There is more to life than exams.

– L.S. Lowry

Yet he had what might least be expected of such a man, a talent for life.

– Frank Kermode in *The Listener*

WAIT!
   I'm coming, Mr Morris! DON'T GO! Oh Mr Morris.
   Oh! Oh!
   It's no use! Not a bit.
   Mr Morris! Come back, don't go, I've slipped!
   Biscuits!
   No use at all. Well, I'm stuck here. Little Laurie's done for now.

                                   *

Slept so badly last night.
   That fiendish dream, I still feel it. About dealers. Horrible. Couldn't paint it. Or could I? A little pencil sketch . . . some

sharks? No. Can't do any of that at all now. It's over. This time really over.

Damn this house! So cold and damp. I just can't move me flippin' knees. And these ridiculous biscuits dropping through the letter box. Kit-Kats!

Well, that's just like Mr Morris, the old rogue.

If only Mr Shaw had stayed a little longer. He had to go home to his family and his tea, of course.

Where's *my* family? No one. Never. My mother died.

Oh mother!

Nobody. Just a garden fence around me. And what a garden! Never been out *there*!

Never liked this house. Cold, damp, ugly. Rooms too small. Station two miles away, taxi three. If I fling m'pocket-book at the door it'll make a bit of noise. And this mucky plate.

No use. Aren't folk at the bus-stop?

ANYONE THERE?

No use. Let's try the leather slippers.

ANY-one there?

It's what I always say. The unmarried man lives like a king but dies like a dog. Oh why won't me knees budge? M'legs are like jelly.

Mother, poor old mother, poor little Laurie needs you. A heap on the floor, it's come to that. A big clumsy good-for-nothing heap on the hall floor. And your clocks ticking away, mother, after all these years. Your Tompion.

Mother.

Why did you have to die so soon, before it started? The success, mother. I'm famous. I'm an RA. They've put me on a postage stamp. Twice refused a knighthood, what do you say to that? Could have been a Companion of Honour!

But I went on being a tramp. Well, you'd gone.

If only I could shift meself to that telephone. A few feet and I could be flat on m'back where I'd want to be, on the old armchair with me feet in the fire.

Damn these clocks.

Tick, tick, tick, tick. Stop!

I'm fed up with it all. I'm just SICK of it all!

*

Uh?

How I could have nodded off in this fix? At least I didn't have that dream again. But why've I just dreamt of old Bernard Taylor?

Bernard Taylor. Bernard Taylor. Good old *Manchester Guardian*. Good to me. He was right of course. No one's ever been righter. My industrial scenes were too dark, that was the problem. You couldn't see the figures against the background. I laid on all the flake-white just to show him, but he was quite right.

Who else has caught the milky Manchester light, sir? Who has caught the colour of the smog? The damp-charged afternoon? The mean streets? Not Vallette. Lowry.

Yes, I've put the industrial scene on the map.

I did my experiment. Six years waiting to see how the white went down. Like making whisky! And how it *did*, a lovely creamy grey-white. Perfect! Even me father thought that was interesting. Paintings won't be at their best till after I'm dead! Well, they won't have to wait long now!

In Pendlebury they laughed at me for thirty years . . .

That posh lady who drove up to m'door here and sent her lackey asking me for a painting, only it had to be one of me *good* ones.

I only do bad ones, I said. Ha, ha!

But I drew the life for twelve years. That's the foundation of it all.

Matchstick men! Hmph! Not matchstick figures, my word sir! They're a *shorthand*. Do they think I couldn't do realistic figures perfectly well if I wanted to? They're not caricatures! People look like that. I've set eyes on them all.

They're figures in motion. Scurrying about. Not so easy.

But I'm stuck here. Where's m'wallet, I'll try flingin' that.

Dreadful companions, clocks!

*

Oh my God, my God! I'm fed up with this. *Fed. Up.*

I'm dying. Won't be long now, really won't, this time.

Why doesn't anyone come? I've so many friends. Or do I mean so few?

Never had a girl, that's all passed me by.

Must remember to tip out those *Playboy* magazines.

And those drawings of Ann. Very peculiar. Why do I do them? Must be going potty.

Nothing's ever *happened* to me. Not till now at any rate.

Shouldn't have built a life round parents. They die. Station Road, Chorley Road, here, retirement. Had a life to get through and I've got through it. Bothering nobody.

Bothering everybody! Bit of an old pest, I suppose. An *inconvenient* object. Yes. Not a very nice man. Well, humanity's the lowest form of animal life, I always say. I'm dying like a dog.

S'pose I could try for one of these biscuits.

*

No one. NOBODY.

Where *are* they? I get a telephone against my will and I can't even get to it. A nice surprise Mrs Swindles'll have in the morning!

What a life it's been! What a plod! The loneliness. Life.

What are we *doing* it for?

I don't blame rent collection. Plodding the streets, visiting the tenants, all the funny people, I got them into pictures sooner or later, nothing wasted.

What did I feel for them?

Loved them for the shapes they made. Loved their caps and shawls and clogs and bowler hats.

Love the pattern the crowd makes when there's been an accident or something. No sentiment in my pictures, sir!

People are like automatons. You watch them eating or running for a bus, it's so funny! They think they can do as they please. But they can't. They're not free, no one is. No more am I.

Pinned to the floorboards! Walking-sticks and trilbies for company. Toppled canvasses. Chocolate biscuits.

Well I may as well have one. Bit of comfort. As good as religion. Crinkly silver foil lying on the floor like my life.

Never had time for sentimentality.

They've all gone away from me. Maud, Kathleen, Doreen, Pat, Carol Ann. They never understood. Only Ann, fascinating Ann, always faithful Ann. With the gorgeous black stuff round the eyes.

And *she* doesn't even exist. But *I've* cut off from them. Always kept apart, kept my friends apart. Always covering up.

Had to! Those Royal Academy people would have been delighted. 'He's just a Sunday painter, we always knew!' They all wanted to write me off. A primitive. But I'm not, y'know! I use simple materials but I'm not a simple man.

Manchester Academy people were even worse! Now they

come knocking at me door. But Mr Rayner's dying, he blurted it right out this afternoon! Mr Shaw didn't know what to say and I said nothing.

I'm demising too.

*

Tick, tick, tick. Mother speaking in all these clocks telling different times.

Never could have married.

Couldn't leave you, bedfast all those years. You had me fast, mother! And I nearly went out of my mind. I couldn't go with anyone after all that. All I could do was paint. Painting got me through. Wonderful way of getting rid of the time.

Now it's me who's floorfast!

Had to stick to that vision. I'd seen all that beauty! I'd not have seen it if I hadn't been lonely.

Twenty years painting the streets of Salford. Wandering streets, day in, day out, like one of the queer folk m'self.

But I loved some of those places almost better than anywhere. The old terrace steps. The footbridge in Ancoats.

You never understood, mother. You'd never even look through your bedroom curtains.

I painted the yachts you said you'd like me to. Lytham St Anne's. And I painted your bedroom, your deathbed. So silent.

Trapped in your world for ever, because of the beauty of the industrial scene, which you wouldn't even look at.

The embarrassment of it all, mother!

*

Dear me, a mouse! And another. My housemates! Come and have a bit of chocolate! Must have been nesting in that old *Financial Times*.

Champion little mice. Quite tame, aren't you? Great breeders. Perhaps you like the smell of old paint?

You've all been nibblin' this stair carpet for years, nothing left of it.

Come and nibble at me, Mr Mouse, I feel like a lump of old cheese.

I could do with just a sip of nice cold tomato soup.

That would be a comfort.

Must be eight now, at least. Pity these clocks are all wrong. Even m'watch has stopped. May as well chuck it at the door.

ANYONE THERE?

No one's coming.

Fiendish February weather. They've all hurried home for their teas. Well, what else is there?

And I've scared the mice off too.

This is *not* what the Iron Duke meant by 'masterly inactivity'.

Can't even put the music on to while away the hours.

*

How did I ever do it, any of it?

Couldn't do it now. It's all over. Not even a tiny sketch now. Too much like hard work. Even the thought of starting makes me feel sick.

Rum business, this art.

Folk always coming here wanting something from me, something for nothing. 'Have you a drawing? Give an opinion on this! Will you sign that?' Nobody asked me to paint, and now everybody's asking me to. And always more industrial landscapes. Well, I've no time for them.

I prefer the solitary figures, they go deeper. Even if no one else thinks so. Excepting the Marshalls of course. And Mr Bloom. But he sold his in the end.

Change my will? Leave my paintings to rot in a museum cellar? Not on your life!

But dear me, I've enjoyed fiddling with m'pencil in my time. Fiddled away thousands of hours. Rubbing with me fingers, night after night, nudging the line, getting the tension in it. With a drawing you can show the tension between people. Painting's different.

Never could paint shadows. So I let it be artificial. Won't use a medium or a glaze.

Never knew what I was going to do with the empty canvas. Knew I'd get something on it by the end of the day, or the night more like. Things just cropped up. Like a dream. A vision.

Getting the balance right, I'm good at that, dear me yes. *Was* good at it. The composition. That's my forte.

Marvellous way of passing the time! Middle of the night, the world's absolutely quiet, *Lucia* on the gramophone, same aria over and over, crackle crackle scratch. I love monotony as well as music.

Not *this* monotony.

Anyone THERE?

Nobody comes when I want them. Only the wind off Saddleworth Moor. Damn that draught!

*

The sun never shines in my pictures. And no one's cheerful. They're all too busy fighting the battle of life. Never happy unless they're drunk. *Father Going Home!*

I've never touched a drop. Didn't dare. Saw what it could do.

All grotesque, my characters – misfits, cripples. Split my sides laughing at them.

But I *do* feel sorry for them. They've had a shock from life. It was too much for them. Whatever they tried to do it baffled them.

And what do I know about warmth and love? *Sex?*

I know about cripples and wasteland and empty houses. Bare boards. Cobwebs. Biscuit wrappers!

People think I'm a cold fish.

But I got the humour in! *The Same Girl Coming Back. Figure of a Girl with the Least Effort.*

All my characters are really me, my mood.

Me the man with red eyes, the man lying on the wall in summer. Me the lost ones on the park bench, the woman with the beard, the cripple on the trolley, the hump-backed girl. Me Ann even.

Me the dog with five legs. Me the dark lonely churches and collieries and houses and ships. All me. My ghosts.

I couldn't be any other way. I couldn't go away from mother and father. Couldn't be sociable. What if I didn't have the talent! I had to find it. I'm a very simple man.

But I'd seen all that beauty of dereliction.

*

A knock? Or am I dreaming? I'm dozing.

Oh I'm going to die.

Why, mother, have I never had the experience? The common experience of humanity!

I've always done just what I wanted to do.

So many nevers! Never been abroad. Never been in a plane. Never driven a car. Never smoked. Never taken *drugs*, my goodness. Not like the young people these days!

But Rossetti took his chloral!

Rossetti's dream women. Proserpine. *His* Ann. Wonderful artist! And they say he couldn't draw!

For me the kissing never began and now I'm utterly clapped out.

There *is* someone out there.

Probably a Moors Murderer!

No. I'm alone in this cold world. With cold macs and trilbies and packing cases. And Mr and Mrs Mouse.

I've lived too long.

It can't all be waste, *can* it? Suffering wherever you turn. I don't understand a thing!

Who'll tell me what it's all about?

There *must* be something after.

*

The cold waves, coming in towards you, nearer and nearer. What if they didn't stop one day but just kept on coming? That *would* be the end of it all.

I must go back to Sunderland and see the sea.

So vast. Generally I'll put nothing on the sea when I paint it. A tiny boat, if I must.

I'll take a taxi. Mrs Marshall will be good to me. Lots and lots of cream and nuts for Little Laurie.

I'm not a bad old chap. Everyone takes me in.

*

Uh?

What's that!

Another dream. Nasty. Stockport viaduct, train half off the side, shrieks . . . sharks . . . monsters . . . people falling into the air . . .

Last of my accident scenes!

Legs are stone cold. Can't shift at all.

This won't do, sir, won't do at all!

Seven walking-sticks in the stand and couldn't walk to save his life! Man Lying on the Floor, that's my story sir, and I'm sticking to it. Someone should do a painting of *me*. House on the Moor. They'd better hurry!

Lonely grey stone house and big round hills like titties. Moors Murderers lurking in the hills. Put in a plume of chimney smoke, if you must.

Lovely Ann inside the house with the black stuff round her big eyes and her hair tied up tight and lots of lipstick on her little red lips.

Lovely Ann in the front bedroom with her long red nails and a great big bow tight tight round her neck. Lovely Ann's in a straitjacket.

Lovely Ann's growing a beard . . .

Oh mother, I'm running out of time!

I don't want to die!

Drifted about for a lifetime and now I'm in a straitjacket. I'm practically in my coffin.

Mother! Since you died the world's been very much too big for me.

Is that too silly sentimental?

*

Come here Mr Mouse, I'll tell you something. I can't *stand* Rembrandt. Loathe him! Too big. Can't get hold of him. He's like life! Frightening. Now take Boudin's beach scenes. Small-scale, but I can get hold of *him*.

What is this greatness anyway? Will *I* live?

What about *my* beach scenes? My fairgrounds. My best work maybe? *Daisy Nook.* Mottram. Peel Park. Piccadilly Gardens. Panoramas. *Bargoed. Ebbw Vale.* Sheer joy of space.

Will it all last?

I'm waiting . . .

It must be long past nine. Past ten.

Space, space, space, give me space! That what it's all about! Pure space. *Daisy Nook.* Space of the imagination. Not the grotesques.

Space that *isn't* me. *Not* my ghosts.

Space opening out.

Light.

Uh?

What's that knocking?

Who's there? Wait! WAIT!

I'm on the FLOOR!

It's you!

Of course, Thursday night! But you don't sound like yourself, Mr Robertson. You don't have a key?

What took you so long anyway?

Well, thank God you've come!

Now I can rest easy.

A Manchester Man

an anecdote

Should I go to the signing or not? Anthony Burgess was due to appear that Saturday morning – it was a beautifully sunny one – at the big university branch of Dillons on Gower Street to launch his *A Mouthful of Air* volume on language and linguistics. Dithering, I went. I don't usually do this sort of thing. Though I like seeing famous authors, fabulous creatures, Olympians descended into our midst, I do not wish to embarrass them with my idiot questions and emotional demands. It is striking how we tend to assume proprietary interest in a famous person, writer or whomever, merely by setting eyes on them, in the street, on a train (as I found once when I entered a carriage occupied by Tom Stoppard), or at a signing. I got to the store a little early and watched preparations being made for the fabulous creature's advent as I breezed about the ground floor. He was to be seated at a table at the foot of the main staircase, directly opposite the main entrance, and a trolley heavily loaded with his works had been wheeled into position. Other writers sign copies of a single book or maybe a clutch of works; but copious Burgess's oeuvre was as a bookshop within the bookshop, a great hive of honey – and we eagerly awaited the arrival of the busy bee.

I drifted to the end of the shop and back across to the discount section and when I returned to the centre-door, there was Burgess installed at the table with pen in hand, a line of signature-seekers, *signees*, already forming, and his bright-garbed wife hovering nearby with a minder (as I presumed). The pen was a sleek felt-tip with a transparent nozzle sheathing a steel-fine point and looked up to the job. How much signing must that hand have done in its time! But how incalculably much more writing! How much typing ribbon mustn't he have punished to a tatter, how many trees' worth of paper put through Qwertyuiop's rollers! He looked quizzically at the trolley, as though bemused by the fact of his prolificacy, picked up a volume or two, snorted. A voice on loudspeakers confirmed the arrival of the 'world-famous author' in readiness to sign, and the first book was proffered.

His wife, I'd heard, was an Italian countess, but she struck my voyeuristic eye as purely bohemian, with a sort of amiable dottiness (I hope I do not offend). As a partner for him she wore a certain air of predestination, I fancied, wondering what it must be like to trundle endlessly with him on the hectic international circuit of signings like these, not to mention readings, lectures, interviews, radio, TV. I suspected she went a good way towards making them fun, actually. (I do not wish to fawn.) She lit a fag.

Both of them were a touch bedizened, I thought. He was got up in an expensive-looking sports jacket of light orange-brown check; a shirt whose reddish pattern, though not its material, was lumberjack-like; navy pants, brown socks, and black buckled shoes. He sported a cravat streaked with orange and pale yellow. Seemingly glued into position, lank strands of light grey hair spanned the ample cranium, which was tufty above the ears. The mouth exercised me: a wry smile seemed ever to play across it, lips forming a hair-fine upward gradient at each side as though facetiously, but in fact involuntarily. Sometimes the lips were smacked in a way that curiously made him seem at once self-pleased and diffident, the contradiction plausibly resolving itself into an effect of twinkling irony. The face was but gently frayed with age; and the complexion notably pale. The wonted cigar was missing.

He spoke in a gruff voice and the remains of a Manchester accent but his manner was not gruff, if the distinction may be allowed. He was ebulliently if efficiently courteous, with a jocose word for everybody; though – further contradiction – I thought I detected something more nearly morose below the surface, attesting the strain of the genial obligation. '*Diabolus in musica*,' Burgess pronounced. Somebody was having a copy of *The Devil's Mode* stories signed. 'Are you familiar with the musical term? No? Very well.' And he muttered to himself, '*Mi contra fa diabolus est in musica*,' as he scratched his name. I debated whether I myself should, or could, present a volume for signing. More anxious dithering; but if I'd come this far, why not go the whole hog? On the other hand, I'd now seen Burgess plain – why not leave it at that? The queue moved constantly but was constant. Should I take one of those brand-new copies of *A Mouthful of Air* from the trolley and join in? 'Ah yes,' Burgess was barking as he flicked through someone else's copy indicating various passages. 'This is of some interest, and also this, hmm.' The statements were perfectly factual, impersonal. I thought, Dammit, I will. And when my turn came to stand by the author and with trepidation I asked, 'How are you?' he replied without hesitation, 'I'm dying. I've just been given a death sentence.'

That should have given me more pause, I suppose, than it did; but flushed with the pleasure of direct contact (and the thrill of meeting the great is close to sexual), I went on audaciously. 'It's not the first time you've had one, is it?'

'No,' he agreed, looking up from my *Mouthful* at me. 'I've been through this before. But this time it's real, I think. What would you like me to write? Just my name?'

I nodded, embarrassed, and as the hard tip went about its work I spluttered: 'Are you writing anything at the moment?'

'I am,' he replied. 'I'm trying to finish a novel about Christopher Marlowe in time for the quatercentenary of his murder next year.'

I mentioned that I'd greatly enjoyed *Little Wilson and Big God*, the first of his two volumes of 'confessions', which embraces a bristlingly detailed, tactile, odoriferous portrait of Manchester life *then*. This was a world sustained by hotpot, tripe and trotters, nutmeggy custards, Eccles cakes, pints of draught Bass, and as I'd noted with an amused remembrance of my own childhood, California syrup of figs; the same world that he brought to fictional life in *The Pianoplayers*. Burgess, famously, was reared a working-class, Mancunian, partly Irish Catholic, suffering slights of rejection all his days – the ache of the outsider, the mild paranoia of one considering himself irredeemably excluded from the London literary establishment, one who attended Manchester University not Oxbridge and felt doomed to be regarded always as plebeian and have his books misprized and deemed too many, far too many. I had been touched by the tone of cheery stoical wistfulness in which he evokes his deprivations and defeats in the *Confessions*. Once – it was the Christmastime after the book was published and I was strolling in a Salford park that looks down on a great silver-grey industrial expanse south and west of Manchester docks – I even in the cold breeze all but shed a tear for Burgess and his poor dishevelled passage through life. And here I was face to face with this Manchester Man.

He was adding the date, '17.10.92', to his confidently etched signature. My time was up, another admirer pressed forward, and Burgess was on to the subject of counting phonemes, leaving me to slope off into the sunny Bloomsbury afternoon more than a mite disconcerted. For had I not been awkward and even importunate? The hoped-for gleam of special sympathy hadn't been forthcoming. I'd been wrong to hanker for it. I'd abused his courteous candour with my shifty proprietorial desires. But he didn't know my name.

*

Should I go via Wakefield or Manchester? I was wondering one dismal afternoon some thirteen months later when business called me to Huddersfield. I plumped for Manchester and it was as the trans-Pennine 'Sprinter' was nearing Stalybridge – blackness was all the windows showed – that I took up my copy of the *Manchester Evening News* and, trying to withstand the distress of the glaring front page about the conviction of two eleven-year-old boys for the murder of an infant, and dismissing a two-page spread about the Manchester-based teeny-bopper group called Take That!, I reached page seven to find the headline: 'Fighting Writer Burgess Loses His Final Battle.' He lost it in London, but for me it was as though he had come home to Manchester.

A Dead Man in Deptford had duly appeared several months earlier; and perhaps he completed as many books in the year of his second death sentence as he managed (five and a half) under the stern admonishment, decades ago, of the first? 'Wedged as we are between two eternities of idleness, there is no excuse for being idle now,' runs the second sentence of *Little Wilson*. How unfussed he had in truth appeared when we had our nugatory encounter and (as I later learned) the fatal bronchoscopy and X-ray prognosis was only two days old! Perhaps veneration can make us oddly callous. But all I'd really wanted to do when I met Burgess was to let him know I bore him love!

Difficulty in Swinton

three paragraphs

When one returns to the parental home as an 'adult', ticklish situations can arise. With what largeness of spirit, what a generous embrace one arrives, after this or that foray into the wider world, back at the familiar paint-chipped kitchen door, one's constant mother concernedly waiting! But the rooms, the ceilings, the furniture, the carpets and conversations lead one inexorably into the old dispensation. Overnight, one's adult skin, too tender, perhaps, sloughs off. Breakfast is the Rice Krispies of childhood, to a similar radiophonic accompaniment. One starts remembering concretely what is was one wanted to escape. One's resistance goes low. It's all a bit existential.

Why, last time I was there, on the second day I innocently accepted my father's offer of a driving lesson! Some clod-heavy black bags of garden rubbish had to be transported to the dump in nearby Swinton. It was only a few minutes' drive but I could do nothing right. He winced, started in his seat, took on an exasperated, pained tone of voice, all but cursed me; while I bridled, clenched, sweated, inwardly raged. We broke our little journey to buy something from the B & Q hardware super-market, this being a discount Wednesday. My father prowled the bays while I moped at the check-out, only to be accosted by a freelance salesman with a slicked moustache and persuasive tongue to whom I ridiculously confided our address. When I admitted as much to my father, he became flustered and worse, and I was furious at seeming so weak.

We drove on along Station Road, where I was keener to look out for Lowry's erstwhile home than for traffic, and into the gravelly open land, by which time we were both whey-faced as one of the painter's clowns. The dumping was the easy bit. I found it in me to assess the view of Manchester under a cool, whitened sky. I was determined to stick out the lesson and get us home in some sort of harmony. But I couldn't, it seemed, get the hang of the old Cortina's clutch. The biting point eluded me. I was doing my best, but my best was worse. My father grimaced, and I felt thoroughly flushed with discomfiture. Odd, therefore, that my legs began to feel cold. I had my eye trained now on the dangerous highway, but glancing down at the pedals I was surprised to see a pair of glabrous limbs in a pair of grey terylene shorts. Shaken and relieved, we alighted into the safety of our tarmacadamed drive, where Mummy, constant at her kitchen door, did not seem so very surprised when I declared, in a voice that had distinctly risen in pitch, and rose still higher to a scream, 'I'll be going back to London TONIGHT!'

Rehearsal

The salutation had to me
The very sound of courtesy

– Wordsworth, 'Stepping Westward'

Lowry often related how 'a boy I knew', accompanying his father to [Manchester] Town Hall on business, came by chance on the great man [Ford Madox Brown] engaged in his work [of painting murals] and was 'addressed most courteously' by the artist.

– Shelley Rohde, *A Private View of L.S. Lowry*

'Barbirolli. *Baar-bir-olli!*' my shaggy, grizzled uncle used to muse out loud as he ate his dinner, mouthing every vowel and consonant of the name with reverent precision, lost in admiration and ambition. He was a bit of a conductor himself, well, a lot of one in his imagination, and he looked the part as well as old JB as he lifted his greasy fork to conduct a bar or two of air.

'Barbirolli's a *star*,' he asserted. 'Stuck with Manchester, when he could have had Noo York for the having. He followed Toscanini, you know.' I knew.

'They sent him a telegram in Noo York – in the middle of the war – saying how would you like to come to Manchester?'

My uncle grins, lips slightly afroth. 'And when he got here, there were twenty players in the band an' a lad.'

'So what did he do?' I knew the answer.

'He went out looking for young, elderly and cripples who could play an instrument.'

My uncle was a member of the Hallé Club and prided himself on getting into rehearsals at the Free Trade Hall to study the Barbirolli approach in close-up. One day he planned to conduct more than his own cigarette smoke. He would start a little choir, he fancied. Meanwhile he needed to refine his stick technique.

He was a retired shop steward with a love of Sibelius. A bachelor, he lived alone in a council maisonette on the cusp of Lower and Higher Broughtons, not far, as it chanced, from Sir John and Lady Barbirolli in the heart of the affluent Jewish area on New Hall Road, premises he admitted he was wont to spy on. 'But I've never yet seen them in,' he regretted. One afternoon he showed me the house, Walton Lodge, a hefty, purply-brick semi-detached mansion with half-timbered gables from which, as uncle suggested, you could probably see the Free Trade Hall on a clear day. But we had no better luck. The place had a patina of silence, a glow of inaccessibility at the end of its short gravel drive.

At school I was dithering between the arts and sciences. I played the cello in the school orchestra, even occasionally in the community orchestra, and was quite keen to develop my musical side – I had a reasonably promising ear; but I liked chemistry and biology too. My father was all for the science side, while his elder brother roguishly tempted me in the other direction. He decided to take me along to the next open rehearsal and give me a taste of professional music-making.

'Of course, it might put you off for life,' he conceded when the arrangement had been settled. 'But you'll get a good look at old JB.'

'At the back of him anyway.'

'They've got Sibelius 1 on the programme, and let's see, something by Bax. Oboe Concerto. Arr. Barbirolli, it says, First Perf. It's Lady Barbirolli playing that, under her maiden name, Evelyn Rothwell. Did you know that?' I did.

My father dropped me at my uncle's early on a Sunday morning in mid-April in the late sixties. He was leaning against one of the thin poles of his shallow porch holding a slim pack of sandwiches in greaseproof wrapping and a pocket-score of the Sibelius symphony – proud possession. We set off at once to catch the first of two buses to the Free Trade Hall, where we were supposed to be in our seats by twenty past ten. The Jewish stores on Cheetham Hill Road were bustling, but Deansgate lay quiet in the sun. Everything about the hall, the steps between the great portico arches, the unmanned foyer, the predominantly empty rows of seats, seemed different from the way I knew it, though my knowledge was confined to a Chetham's School speech-day concert to which I'd been taken by a friend's family and, I think, just two 'Hallé nights' – my first encounters with Tchaikovsky's symphonies. We turned up early, so my uncle stepped out again for a cigarette, leaving me in the stalls absorbing the equally novel *indoor* atmosphere of this Sunday morning.

*

There were a few other spectators scattered across the main block of the stalls, perhaps Hallé Clubbers. At one of the concerts I'd attended – with another friend, whose aunt had a pair of subscription season tickets which she frequently couldn't use – the *Daily Telegraph*'s critic had been pointed out to me as he took his seat, but it was empty now. I recalled an embarrassing moment during the same concert when the man immediately in front of us had swivelled round to give unsought advice on the pronunciation of a soloist's name. 'Not John Og*din*. Og*don* with an o, not an *i* or an *e*!' he had stated, adding: 'And please. No more chattering during the music!' I gazed up at the narrowing balconies on either side of the rear part of the platform, surprised as previously that there was room enough for a person to sit in there; and my eye travelled up and down the enormous wood-panelling of the back wall, resting on the Corporation's coat of arms, a Lion and Unicorn with the motto *Concilio et Labore*, doubtless intended as the hall's cynosure – but that was always going to be John Barbirolli on his podium.

He had not yet entered, nor had my uncle, but the harp player was on the platform engrossed in a tuning process, likewise the timpani player. Attendants were shifting stands and the librarian (as I presumed) was filling folios. A couple of double-bass players took their places, a horn player took hers, then an oboist came on piping a flurry of scales. The stroke of half past ten was like a magnet to the players. From out of sight they flew to their places and suddenly all was assembled, the complete constellation, in civis, enveloped in its own cacophony: the leader, Martin Milner, at his desk; the first flute Roger Rostron – I remembered the name – at his; and Barbirolli emerging from the stage-door to the right, tottering with fag in mouth to his position, where he slumped on to his seat and promptly extinguished the fag.

I took the opportunity before my uncle returned to move us forward into the front block of stalls, the better to scrutinize our hero. He was sealed in a neat velvet jacket and turquoise polka-dot cravat. In the breast pocket of the jacket he wore a silk handkerchief and on the little finger of his left hand a ring with a large gaudy stone; there was a jewelled stud in his lapel. His face was pale, somehow both fleshy and drawn, his nose and lower lip prominent; the hair, grey and copious, slicked back in long lank strands; the expression sympathetic, gentle, quizzical, determined. There was something about his face that reminded me of a television personality. But who? The comedian Spike Milligan, was it? Spike Milligan got up as the woozy eccentric Beachcomber? No, that was unfair. JB's appearance was imbued with poetry, he was a genuine artist.

My uncle returned just as JB gave his metal music-stand a couple of sharp raps of the baton and got out the score – my uncle that is – of Sibelius's first symphony and looked approvingly at the first page and sidelong at me. I knew the work from a bulky set of 78s which I'd bought at a marvellous little surprise of a second-hand record shop in a hidden square behind Market Street, and was poised for that eerie E minor clarinet solo, arising out of nowhere – out of the mundane Manchester Sunday morning in fact – but as if from behind the rising mists of a far north country, to the faint background of rumbling timpani. Cheerily, JB spoke his first words of the morning fully audible to me; he made a smoker's croak that was more like a throat-clearing to precede his words than the utterance itself:

'Take it from de beginning.'

Another rap. I thrilled as (remaining seated) he lifted his long thin baton and with both hands gave the first beat. But instead of the magical evocative sounds of the north I heard a side-drum rap, a softly struck cymbal and a stretch of solemn preamble to something – a something that suddenly proved to be a perky, down-to-earth figure in the violins. I looked at my uncle and he grinned at me, whispering: 'John Ireland, *London Overture*. Clean forgot to mention it!'

Well, this went pretty smoothly, a jolly, mock-solemn piece with a poignant middle section and which I liked at once. After a run-through Sir John asked for the beginning again, telling the orchestra that the insouciant phrase had to be cheekier. It was *Dilly, Piccadilly, Piccadilly!*, the cry of a Cockney bus-driver.

'Ah'm a Cockney m'self, so ah *know*,' he said, emphasizing that last word. The orchestra tried to oblige him. Almost instantly he rapped the stand. 'More clipped. Throw it away.' They tried again, then once more. They threw it away. This time he stopped them with a smile.

'Now *that's* something like an omnibus. Takes me right back to m'Edwardian childhood.'

And suddenly he coughed his poor insides out. He was so fragile, for all the decisiveness of his bearing. His face easily relapsed into the haggard set of someone who had been up all the previous night and quite possibly the night before that.

'Let's turn to de Bax,' he called out now.

The wind and percussion players went off, leaving a string orchestra. He was not in good health, perhaps only will-power kept him going. And how odd his accent was, part Italian-Cockney, part educated and orotund, and by now a good part Manchester!

An attendant was setting up Lady Barbirolli's music-stand as she entered with her instrument and its case to the applause-like tapping of bows on stands. Also audible was a crockery-clatter coming through the door at the left side of the platform. I was surprised, too, that a certain amount of *sotto voce* talk by people in the hall was kept up during the try-outs. But perhaps they were big-wigs. JB looked radiantly pleased at the end of this nearly unbroken run-through; exchanged smiles with his wife and announced that they had all played 'with great sensitivity' and would start the break a little bit early. More bow-taps.

*

Uncle and I considered the possibility of trespassing into the green room to try and get a cup of tea or perhaps a chat with one or other of the players. I thought to myself how wonderful it would be to talk with Sir John himself. But we contented ourselves with eating our few sandwiches on the portico steps and strolling in the mild sunshine along Peter Street. We turned left near the massive sooty edifice of the Great Northern Railway Company's Goods Warehouse and walked along Fountain Street towards Central Station, Uncle ceaselessly imparting information, not all of it familiar.

'Of course, they'll have already probably had two full rehearsals for this programme as usual at the Zion Institute, somewhere over there,' he said, and pointed in the direction of Hulme, a maze of mean streets into which I had once ventured.

'Zion Institute' sounded exotic, alarmingly so. He tried to name all the previous conductors of the Hallé, but could think of only three – Sir Charles Hallé himself, Hans Richter and Sir Hamilton Harty – and explained how the orchestra had had to hold its concerts at Belle Vue Circus during the war years, up until the bombed Free Trade Hall was rebuilt.

'That would be in 1951,' he recollected, pursing his lips.

He told me a few things about Central Station too, for instance how there's an underground passage connecting it to the grand Midland Hotel opposite.

We headed back to the hall along Lower Mosley Street, but found we'd dawdled too long. We'd barely sneaked in through the doors of the shuttered-up café at the back of the auditorium when that eerie clarinet tune and kettledrum rumble came floating down the aisle to greet us. We took the nearest seats. There was an abrupt tremolando summons from the violins, and what I knew to call the 'first subject' – a short breath and a splutter – was given out. But Barbirolli punished his stand, grunted at the violas and cellos:

'Too soon! It's not together! Once again.'

They did it again. Another rap.

'A little more crescendo! Again!'

Slowly, more laboriously and sternly now, the rehearsal proceeded. There was a big climax. The second subject – a sunglint of flutes on water – came and went. 'More marcato!' was JB's passing comment. A loudening accelerating passage was negotiated. 'In one!' bawled Barbirolli. The players on the front desk of first violins had a sweet little dialogue, and a melody bubbled up beneath them on bassoon. We were in the region of development – fragments of themes were being airily tossed about. Little striding figures for pizzicato strings peculiarly reminded me of the 78 discs with their brown-paper smell in the shop near Market Street. Scales for woodwind and lower strings slithered in opposite directions. The harpist did her fluttering thing.

The orchestra was constantly stopping and starting. Sir John was satisfied with little, sometimes beating time with his baton on the stand, sometimes half-singing the phrasing he was after: *dah de da-i-ah-i dah di.*

'Give the dotted notes the full vay-lue,' he enjoined the violins and violas, shortening the first vowel of 'value' in an old-fashioned way.

Then, frowning, to the basses: 'The G's too loud!'

At one point Martin Milner interrupted him with a question which I couldn't quite hear, but judging from his gestures, it was about bowing. My uncle hissed to me, 'JB puts in all the bowing marks himself. Famous for it.' He, Sir John, gave his opinion on the matter with a forceful upbow of air and Milner appeared to be satisfied, for he turned round to pass the decision to the other first violins, who reached for their pencils, and from there it was relayed across the string department.

A sudden rush of scales ushered in a huge, oh a wonderful climax, the main theme proudly recapitulated by the brass. Barbirolli seemed to like it, at any rate, shouting, 'Good, good. A bit more!' over the din; then there was an abrupt falling away of the sound, and a something trying to emerge. It was the solo clarinet from the outset. Barbirolli didn't like this. He struck his desk.

'No. The dynamics are rather complicated here. Bassoon and horns go down, strings swell up *at de same time*. Then a little pause. Then strings right down to pianissimo and, first clarinet, you've got to come in tremendously softly. As if you were trying to be *born*! Once again.' A rap. 'From the *tutta forza* chord. I won't measure exactly de bars.'

They did these bars again and the effect was instantly intensified. JB exclaimed approval and conducted on to the end of the movement: another accelerating climax, a solemn full-brass blare, the strings scrubbing, the timpani crackling, loud-ening, retiring, and two resonant, fatefully terminal plucked chords from violins, violas and harp. *Plipp. Plopp.*

*

I felt utterly in the grip of the music, as the second movement followed with its sad lilt and tolling bass-note in the harp; then the bright explosion of the scherzo; and the impassioned declamation of a strangely familiar tune initiating the finale, subtitled *Quasi una Fantasia*, as I noticed from uncle's score. Uncle was gripped too – he abstractedly scratched his shock of hair, but half-way through this last movement was prompted to creep out of the hall, he didn't say why. The orchestra began a fugue, and I thought I was seeing things, but, yes, Sir John had quitted the podium and was hobbling off the platform while the players were in full flight, indicating the remaining fugal entries as he went. By the time he entered the auditorium they had reached a forceful tutti which they executed with assurance, managing admirably without him, though he was conducting perfunctorily and humming croakily as, with a look of listening intently, he advanced along the central aisle, passing a couple of people at the end of rows, towards *me*!

I saw the cravat and stones in close-up, the big nose and droopy lower lip, a faint resemblance to an aunt of mine incongruously striking me. The features looked so extremely well-worn but were *alight*. He turned to face the orchestra at precisely the point at the rear of the hall where I was sitting, then beamed sidelong at me and somewhat gruffly inquired:

'How does it sound from here, young man? How's de balance?'

I must have looked very surprised.

He was a small man and seemed immense. And *kind*. I couldn't even get out a mumble of words.

'Are you *fond* of Sibelius?'

His words exploded in my heart. He set off back to his proper place, conducting more vigorously now – the movement's big tune was throbbing forth *cantabile e largamente* – and securely reinstalled himself on the podium for the final climax (my uncle had slipped back in now) and I glowing with the experience. I felt flustered but favoured, blessed even. It had all happened in the time taken to smoke a cigarette. Poor Uncle would be chagrined to learn what he had missed. A terse little

figure was being spelled out treble forte, the strings in semiquav-
ers essayed the heights and depths, the three conclusive sforzato
wind chords were reached, on the third of which the timpani
roll rapidly diminished in volume and those two fateful pizzicato chords, quieter now, without the harp, returned inexorably
to complete the formal scheme.

Plipp. Plopp.

I shivered. There was brief silence before the baton clacked
against the metal stand for the last time that morning. Barbirolli
uttered a subdued 'Thank you, ladies and gentlemen,' and
seemed to crumple up. The players dispersed with fantastic
rapidity.

*

'Well, it's something you can treasure all your life,' my uncle
was saying as we tripped along Peter Street to the bus-stop on
Deansgate. 'It's a great honour. That man's sacrificed everything
for his music. And for this city. Had plenty of offers, but he's
stuck it out with us.'

'It was a marvellous performance,' I ventured. 'I mean,
rehearsal. I wish we could come back tonight for the actual
concert.'

'Another time and we will.'

'Did you hear the way he pronounced it: *Sibeli-oos?*' I
irrelevantly inquired.

'Look there's a bus for us!' And we hastened, uncle saying, 'If we don't take too long getting back, I'll do us some
spaghetti.'

Which wasn't a particularly enlivening prospect after the
morning's deep stirring fascinations. My uncle fancied himself
as a bit of a cook, and though he could indeed run to a tolerable
spaghetti or stew, he always worried me with his habit of

peering into the simmering pan with a cigarette in his mouth and chucking in a promiscuous variety of sauces. In fact I found my plate of pasta perfectly edible, while Uncle ate so voraciously and talked so eagerly – he was in excellent spirits – that he wouldn't have noticed or minded a dusting of ash.

'So you want to be a scientist?' he taxed me more than once that afternoon.

'I think I do.'

'Nothing wrong with that. It's a noble calling. But do you want to be spending all those hours in a laboratory with smelly chemicals.'

'I don't say I *necessarily* want to be a chemist.'

'You want to keep clear of anything to do with factories, I'll tell you that.'

He'd finished sucking spaghetti and was sucking on a cigarette when the doorbell rang. I was left for a moment with the greasy plates and the ancient painting of the loch on the wall in front of me.

'I was just saying,' Uncle said with a cough as he let my father in, 'that he should stay well clear of the whole grimy awful world of industry.'

He hadn't been, actually. Our conversation had threaded its way back to 'Glorious John' and the fine points of the morning's session via the detours of London, Germany, the war, pacifism, the problem with the Labour government, the BBC's Third Programme, choral conducting, the music of Vaughan Williams.

But that's my uncle for you, never misses a chance.

'I can guess what you'd advise instead,' my father said.

'Well, he is a person of musical sensitivity.' He pronounced the last word with short precise *i*'s, oddly like Barbirolli.

'And how did the rehearsal go?' my father asked me.

'He said something to me,' I blurted out. 'He came up and spoke.'

My dear old uncle, moistly grinning, thumped the table-mat triumphantly.

'Who did?' my father asked, half removing his coat. 'You don't mean Barbirolli?'

'*Baar-bir-olli!*'

Ethics and Aesthetics
of Grandmother

While the generations boiled down to one
And the kettle burned dry
In a soon grandmotherless room

– Norman Nicholson, 'Have You Been to London?'

1. Tick. Tock. Tick. Tock. The pauses between the tick-tocks seem enormously longer than a second. The grandfather clock, dark walnut streaked with pale, ticks on when no one's in the room to hear it, companion and symbol of the lonely, foster-father of silence and slow time. Tick. Tock. Tick. Tock. Tick. Tock.

2. A slip of a girl, no more than four, with a sweet intelligent face and thick brown heavy fringe, stands on a ruffled patch of beach, her feet in girlish sandals touching, hands behind her back, tummy slightly protruding in a tight-fitting stripy seaside dress, and offers the camera an expression marginally too composed to be a smile. It is an old box camera, wielded by a man of whom he's never seen an image; and it seems as if she stood in the most remote and mythical world, a world over-whelmingly *before*. He doesn't suppose this beach could be

much farther afield than North Wales – perhaps Prestatyn or only the familiar haunts of Blackpool or Bispham: they never went far. She resembles even at that age his mother now, her half-sister, who never saw her, she – the first-born – being dead from diphtheria a few months after the photograph (all that survives of her) was taken. His grandmother, who constantly spoke of her late second husband, his grandfather, never once in his hearing referred to the loss of this airy, sensual waif; but his mother told him that she had found it so agonizing that she wished never to have another child.

3. She had, of course, had his mother, and acquired a step-daughter when she married the widower brother of her first husband, a marriage necessarily delayed until the country's punctilious incest laws were perforce liberalized after the erasure of a male generation in the trenches. She herself had come from a family of rather more children than anyone seemed able to number: he only knew Vera, the plump, slower-witted, lisping one who had never escaped her elder sister's protective clutches, not even by going into service (with a most benign local family); and Ernest, the model of a spick-and-span, hob-nailed, smiling uncle, as genial as the day is long. Grandmother saw little of him, and less of the siblings whose names he as a child occasionally picked up from adult conversations – were there really a Tom, Dick and Harry? – and who appeared to be strewn over Wales. She had, it seemed to him, little or no interest in her own background, and an apparent obliviousness to the momentous twentieth-century events, the wars (right back to the Boer), the social and technological revolutions she had lived through. She had knitted through them, reserving her interest for the immediate family in the immediate present. And so, as he often reflected, she had not grown wise, never

herself *reflected* on anything. Still, she had always been kind, decent, respectable – a most unlikely person to be affected by an incest law! Anyone can surprise, though. When rummaging through a musty carton of books and documents years after her death, he plucked out her birth certificate and concluded from certain irregularities that she may have been illegitimate.

4. That would certainly have been tricky for her if it had come out in her early life, in those times of social correctitude; her second husband was a pillar of the community. A quiet, tall, stooping, spare, dignified man, with a large bald oval cranium, a long thoughtful chin, and a full upper lip that lent him a quizzically serious expression in photographs, he was gently spoken, highly considerate, and badly bronchitic. He had a solid job running the stationery office at the Town Hall, but was also a lay preacher – for twenty-one years minister of an Independent Methodist church – a member of the League of Temperance, and a Freemason: no less solid pursuits. He was unlike his wife in almost all respects – she garrulous, eagerly sociable, concerned with appearances; he reserved, bookish, intellectual. But she understood his needs – as he hers – and had limitless admiration for his mind. There again, it gave her an ideal social position as the minister's wife. She loved entertaining, having people dropping round, the intricate bustle of the church calendar. She missed it all so badly after he died.

5. As a grandfather his tenure was exemplary but brief, only about two and a half years, which was not long enough for his grandson to remember him, though he tried and tried, half-convinced that emanations of the actual man and not just of his photographs were accessible to his memory. But nothing fleshly would quite stick, however much he racked his brain. 'You

were a little divil,' his grandmother would remind him, reminiscing about his very early years. 'A little divil. Your gran'pa thought the world of you. You used to play with his watchchain. He couldn't take you on his knee, you just stood between his legs and dangled his watchchain. It was as though you knew.' (He had always to resist a lamentable smirk of post-Freudian knowingness when she went on in this vein.) 'It was as though you knew. Never lived to see your sister. Oh, a proper little *divil* you were. He could never sit you on his knee.'

6. What remains of him is an example, respected by all the family, of dignified suffering (he had also, as a young man, lost an eye reaching for a too heavy volume on too high a shelf), of kindliness, and devotion to the written word, which he served as book collector, sermon writer and stationer. His daughters thrilled to visit his office, packed with reams of paper, notepads, pencils, pens, clips, blotters, filled with stationery's distinctive warmth. His sermons didn't survive, only a big, bound, dark-blue scrapbook, with 'Literary Diary' printed on the spine, containing the odd reflective paragraph, pasted-in letters and local newspaper cuttings. The books, nearly always bearing his fine-print nameplate with its friendly versified caution to the borrower ('If thou art borrowed by a friend/ Right welcome he shall be,/ To read, to study, not to lend,/ But to return to me'), survived, some of them, for years in quiet front rooms for which his grandmother had sadly little use. *Miracles* by C.S. Lewis; an 1840 edition of George Wither's poetry, autographed by a Wesleyan schismatic of that time, Revd James Everett; Bibles large and small; an octavo Masonic codebook bound in black leather; Marie Corelli's *Thelma*; a long run of the annual *Friendship Book of Francis Gay*; a paperback copy of Patience Strong's *Echoes from a Quiet Corner* (this latter belonging to his

grandmother): they all sat dustily undisturbed in a rickety brown bookcase bearing a little black plastic calendar, ever out of date, in rooms haphazardly furnished and echoing the tick tock, tick tock of that more enduring grandfather.

7. His grandmother knew how to cope. Decades of solitary life didn't break her; and against later images of a soft docile shrunkenness should be set a telling, triumphant mid-life photograph of a brisk, even tall, young mother with pram leading daughters, sister, sister-in-law (they're struggling worriedly to keep up) along the main street of Bispham on some urgent holiday mission. She is clearly a forceful character, a problem-solver. In her plain round scholarly spectacles she strikes him as surprisingly like a blue-stocking or a suffragette. She is wearing a buttoned-up thick coat of the 1930s – the weather must have been its usual. She looks like one who would have searched out and found amusements for the children when it rained.

8. Three removals she endured after Grandpa's decease, and the four houses – inwardly the same (grandmotherly), outwardly marking a steady decrease in respectability and size – were as stations of his maturing. She stayed on for several years in the first, a blunt-porched, fairly roomy semi-detached on hilly Castleway, with jutting front windows mixing vertical and horizontal panes (a feature of the road) and back garden overhung by the leafy mysterious high grounds of Pendleton High School for girls. He played gaily there, discovering new things, new infant niches all the time. The neighbouring house was a yard lower than his grandmother's: he had forever to resist the temptation to jump down on to friendly Mr Foulkes's tarmac drive. Inside the house were candied places, for his grandmother was a specialist in sweets beyond the call of

grandmotherly duty. She sold them for the church and ran the confectionery booth at each December's Christmas Fayre. It was delightful enough to be given blocks of chocolate regularly, but ecstatic when he sometimes stumbled on the storage place of whole *boxes* of blocks. There would also be screwtopped glass jars of sweets as in a real sweet shop: Nuttall's Mintoes, Trebor Mint Imperials, stiff-wrapped Pascall Fruit Bonbons, Cadbury's Chocolate Eclairs, buttermint bonbons by Craven's of York, Keiller's little gold oblongs of butterscotch, and her favourite of all, Callard & Bowser's Brazil Nuts, those sticky arcing orange-brown blobs, each in its twist of grease-proof wrapping – *they* were predictably to be found at the messy base of her handbag years after the stall was discontinued, the church and its planky meeting hall demolished.

9. She had ITV before his mother and father got there, she would always be a devotee of the channel. He watched his first advertisements – the jingle of the Veno's Snowman tickled him – and Yogi Bear cartoons in her house, before being collected by his parents at the end of the long afternoon, recalled to the more normal, proper world of the BBC. They were close, his grandmother, whom he was enjoined to call his Nana, and he; so much so that he always found it difficult to describe her appearance, just as he cannot to this day easily recall the features of his mother's face. The sun shone on their quiet kitchen intimacy, the grandfather clock ticked.

10. He could nevertheless exert himself to suggest that his grandmother had a rounded, soft, bespectacled face, with a small smooth nose whose bob cried out for, and was usually granted, powder; hair dark brown, brushed back when younger, grey and permed when older; a slightly drooping lower lip,

which was readily taken up into a radiant grin. In early and middle life she wore frameless inexpensive glasses; later a dearer, more 'fashionable' sort, with pointed frames. She never overdid the jewellery. She was of small to medium height, round-shouldered, slight but lean, with a proud, determined walker's stride. She often smelled of perfume, but how describe that? In summer she wore soft blouses frilled with lace; in winter most likely a twin set knitted by herself. She had oddly masculine, hefting hands, with thickly veined wrists and kind, knuckly fingers: her hands suggested depth of character.

11. Nana – oh dear, he was too soon embarrassed by the word, all the more so when, much later, he discovered it was a working-class, northern endearment – Nana moved to a smaller house, cheaper and easier to run, up on a large thirties estate bordering Pendlebury, but it proved awkwardly distant from the family centre, and she needed above all to be able to 'slip round' to her daughter's of a morning. What he remembered of this short residency was a new, inadequately explored, small but complicated garden; a nearby spacious dumping ground commanding a view over Manchester and the Pennines; and a pair of mirrors facing each other across the sitting room, giving an impression of infinity. A dull Christmas afternoon was spent in that infinity, the family, against tradition, going to her rather than she coming to them. A day or two afterwards he was taken there again after an outing to the cinema. Her house was instantly absorbed by his imagination into the expansive world of the *Swiss Family Robinson*. She was not at all happy in Beverley Road.

12. More convenient but pokier, darker, more primitive (with only an outside lavatory and the bath having to double as a

kitchen work-surface) was the house on Park Street, off Brazil Street. 'Off Brazil Street' – how many times didn't he write that on picture-postcards sent from holidays over the next decade or more? Brazil Street was the short distance between Claremont Road and the villagey shopping centre on Bolton Road called the Height, and had just a few private houses on it plus the yard walls of a couple of Height shops and the bricked side of a clothing factory. Park Street was cut perpendicularly between Brazil Street and Torrens Street and consisted of two tight terraces with a fenced strip of garden for each house and a rough, stony path between the fences, an unusual feature. There was more chance of neighbourly intercourse here than at Nana's previous address, and she seemed to like the new house for all its limitations: another being the lack of a street view from her sitting room. House, streets and the Height itself are utterly erased now. A 'Discount Giant' and its enormous car park occupies the ground. Someone is forever positioning a vehicle on her silvery biscuit barrel.

13. To sample that barrel's contents – ginger biscuits, fig biscuits, Morning Coffee, glamorous brandy-snaps – he and his mother made their regular Wednesday visits. Wednesday became her day in the archetypal sense in which the BBC children's television programme *Bill and Ben* also defined it. He would trudge home for lunch from school to her house during term-time and back again through the park which on both outward and return journeys was infused with hushed, boring Wednesday-ness. His mother made out that she too was bored to go round, but always kept up conversation when they were there, not that Nana needed prodding. Naturally talkative, she was ever starved of conversation. (She didn't acquire a telephone until very late in life.) While they chattered, and the

familiar names of Nana's Derby and Joan or Women's Auxiliary friends or foes – Mrs Spector, whom he knew was a thin and severe woman; Mrs Davidson, jolly and fat – were bandied about to his mother's forbearing dismay, he sought to amuse himself around the house. The front room with its books, which never managed to interest him though he'd scan them eagerly each time; the two rooms at the top of the narrow stairs, one an unused guest room – a tumble of stale bedding and old furniture – the other Nana's own bedroom. This room, with its nooks and crannies, its genteel, lavender-scented air of privacy, seemed to stretch far back in time. On the glass top of the ornately moulded dressing table, whose multiple mirrors let him peer at the back of his head, lay vials of perfume with wrinkled squeeze-sacs, an assortment of brooches, earrings and necklaces, a ladies' wristwatch whose thin strap was elasticated joints of golden metal, and whose face was almost too tiny to read, a scalloped-edged porcelain dish of tempting money, a photograph of himself as a beaming baby, one of elderly Grandpa, the one of the lost child.

14. Nana, he discovered, was profoundly able to irritate his parents. How she did this he wasn't always exactly sure, but it must have been things she said, things she insisted on (ITV if she came to their house for tea), her possessiveness with her daughter and the family, her sulks and simple ruses in that cause, the time taken up by her often mawkish morning chats, her sheer blatant dependency and the guilt it induced in his mother – guilt can be maddening as well as guilty. At table she invariably talked with her mouth full, addressing remarks to his father which he had no wish to hear – 'How is it going now at your business? Mrs Spector's son-in-law's business is not going well' – in a gobbly manner he found off-putting. She would go

on and on about her favourite television quiz-masters, Michael Miles and Hughie Green, with a soppy gullibilty. And her bad habits did not stop with the voluntary. She was prone to break wind unawares, sometimes in a crackling sequence, like summer weather, reducing him and his sister to stifled paroxysms. It was an unruly odour that, like certain heady perfumes, reliably brought her back for him in years ahead, he was ashamed to admit.

15. Awareness of these faults made him more reluctant to go and see her than he would be in any case – boys being loath to spare their free time for such duties, especially when gardening help is involved – but whenever he went he was surprised at how much he enjoyed himself. Left to flow unimpeded, her talk had a bracing colloquial vigour that he relished, albeit only part-consciously; a salty proverbial directness he knew was long out of date and could never precisely hold in his head afterwards. She was hugely loving, and though she decently reined in her ardour he inevitably ended by transferring his loyalties temporarily from parents to grandparent, not that collusion was sought. Arriving glumly at her front door, hoping that the silence following his ring meant that she was unexpectedly out, but presently descrying through the window her figure looming against the frosted glass of the sitting room door as she fumbled to admit him, he would leave the house an hour or so later with dancing enthusiasm for the grandmotherly cause, all set to proselytize for her when he got home. This or that bright thing he would excitedly relay to his parents, who would seem pleased though managing discreetly to put the dampers on him. And whenever he went out to his grandmother, a feeling of cloying embarrassment was soon enough arrived at. Once the family with grandmother were driving back from a day at the Cleveleys

seaside. The possibility of a return trip to the area was discussed; this time it would be a whole week in Bispham. 'When we're driving there, I want to sit with Nana,' he had passionately declared, and almost straight away knew he was being yucky, not that he had the word. The embarrassment of that moment was apt to recur like a rash. But the saddest example of their intimate conspiracy was his twenty-first birthday. All his life till then she had been anticipating it, telling him what would happen then, how he would be grown-up and could do all sorts of things – marry, get a job – and how all this would be 'champion'. But when the occasion arrived he was a student stuck at home in the long vacation, deprived of his peers, feeling disgruntled and self-pitiful (no party, few presents). She came bouncing round with a parcel in the morning and sat beside him on the small green sofa in the lounge, all smiles. He was aghast to think that this supposedly great event of life amounted to so screamingly little. She rose to the occasion as fully as she was able, and he was only longing to get away.

16. Embarrassment increasingly became the normal emotion associated with her, fast overtaken by pathos. In public she could be excruciatingly indiscreet, handing over family details to the merest stranger, stating family achievements with a boastful abruptness that seemed nonetheless allowed for, in her eyes, by the unwritten rules of respectable old ladies' talk. Old ladies should be suffered by their juniors to effuse over son-in-law and grandchildren, according to those rules. And when rouged cheeks and beaded hairpins meet their like, old lady with old lady, there will properly be a vying for the lethally sly disclosure of family triumph. The excruciation was worse for his mother, and at its worst on Christmas Eve family outings to the Library Theatre in Manchester, when getting everyone down

the plush aisle to their places meant restraining Nana from introducing herself to half a dozen; and when she would pipe up in the middle of the play not with inquiries about what was being said but to report something Mrs Davidson had said at the Auxiliary last week. Long gone the times when she would confidently take him out herself for an afternoon in town with a cosy confab in the womblike Paulden's café; or whisk him of a morning through that shady 'secret' passage near her house to reach Langworthy Road and a delicious wafting of bakery smells. Did the passage still exist?

17. In private the embarrassments were mixed with a mild mocking cruelty on his and his family's part which they found particularly distressing in retrospect. The poor grandmother, packed off home alone after the theatre expedition of the night before, would eagerly return to the family's bosom on Christmas midday dolled up, scented, and dragging behind her a pillowcase out of which presents were already spilling, their clumsy wrappings half-off. With what simple delight she dispensed her gifts! This, of course, would be the morning's second distribution of largesse, the dawn encounter with bulging pillowcases and properly wrapped gifts counting for very much more in his and his sister's eye; but these later presents had generally been bought by their mother on Nana's behalf and thus were keenly anticipated for all that the ritual of their giving was an occasion for furtive giggles. Further giggling, or perhaps a burst of adolescent anger, as she sat upright with a seraphic look of sympathy when the Queen came on the television at three. At Christmas dinner she would try to enjoy herself while the others would wince. She'd take a small glass of cream sherry. Reaching across the table he'd pull a cracker with her. She'd hint at televisual preferences. The wishbone would be duelled over; the parson's

nose, her favourite bit of the bird, readily be put her way. He'd sneak a knowing look at his mother after Nana had left the table and parked herself in a fireside chair. Years afterward he woke from a dream in tears. In it he had had a crystal-clear vision of Nana returned from the grave to their kitchen. 'What would you think of me if I *hadn't* seen through you all, laughing at me?' she had said, smiling peaceably. 'But if only she *had* seen through us,' he thought on waking, 'if only she had! And how could we have ever been so rotten?'

18. 'We need be careful how we deal with those about us, when every death carries to some small circle of survivors, thoughts of so much omitted, and so little done – of so many things forgotten, and so many more which might have been repaired, that such recollections are among the bitterest we can have. There is no remorse so deep as that which is unavailing; if we would be spared its tortures, let us remember this, in time.' Thus Dickens in *Oliver Twist*. True sentiments! and not unworthy of *The Friendship Book of Francis Gay*. Nana was decidedly sentimental. She always took the printed inscriptions in birthday and Christmas cards at face value. Nearly everyone she met in the shops on the Height or, later, at Salford Precinct, or wherever, was 'a nice man'. The only lodger she ever had was nicer than nice, and he was a 'darkie', a visiting student from Sierra Leone (at a time when dark skins were rare enough to be shocking). He lived with her for six months, swore he'd write, and she never heard from him again. Women were more rarely appraised or mentioned. The proprietress of the nearest local wool shop was generally found wanting (her stock too small, her manner slack); but the lady who ran the travel agency, a Mrs Godbiere, famous for sophisticated spectacles and carpet slippers, won endless plaudits for fixing up Nana and Vera with

their package holidays to Eastbourne, though she never had the honour of an accurate pronunciation of her name. 'That Mrs Goddibeer is such a nice person, you know,' he could hear her telling his mother against the background of some surging Mantovani number, perhaps the jaunty *Elizabethan Serenade*, emitted from the wireless and filling their boxy dining room with space. 'She says the chara makes a *number* of stops on the way. We've to go for the tickets tomorrow afternoon, she says. Well, that fits in. Vera's coming round the precint with me.' He points out, exasperated, that the word is *precinct* with a *c*. She smiles and doesn't comprehend.

19. Frequently during his childhood Nana and Aunty Vera, the slender and the stout, would 'sit in' when his parents went out for the evening. He hated such occasions, feeling somehow demeaned by them, knowing Nana could not easily prevail over him, but not thinking defiance in such matters as bedtime (admittedly a more pressing concern in summer than in winter) was worth the trouble, and resenting the fact. Vera was even more ineffectual, ruefully under her elder sister's thumb. Bed-time supper was never quite right. The wrong television pro-grammes were watched. At least there'd be a supply of sweets. Vera's favourites were Bassett's Liquorice Allsorts, which defined her as irrevocably as her lisp. Hope had been early abandoned that Vera would ever be cajoled into actually cohabiting with Nana, who needed a companion increasingly badly, and longed in secret, it was pretty clear, to be invited permanently into her daughter's household. Daughter desper-ately didn't want that.

20. In her own frail household she goes on, goes on, complain-ing but little. Tick. Tock. Tick. Tock. People come. People go.

Few people, in fact; and going more than coming: they all seem to bring with them warning of their imminent departure, its preliminary tang. Lifelong friends fall off, as if afraid a little too much will soon be required of them. Her brothers and sisters are nearly all dead. Ernest's wife, with whom she used to exchange weekly visits, has mysteriously taken agin her. There are her two daughters (but one lives in Scotland) and Vera. Seated by the window looking on to the tiny yard, with her knitting on her knee, frayed quiver of extra needles and the necessary balls of wool at her feet, *Woman's Own* and *TV Times* in the magazine rack, she fills her room with grandmother. She has always been physically resilient; free in her grandchild's eye, from the very possibility of illness, an absolutely constant feature of the landscape. But she increasingly feels her age. She is more than ever insistent on the shutting of doors. The electric fire is always firing all rockets, whereas previously she wouldn't hear of switching on the expensive second bar. Housework is neglected with a new thoroughness. As her daughter will attest, she has never been much of a duster, and her slovenliness is much worsened by failing eyesight: she can't *see* the muck, nor find the 'doings', as she calls the mechanical dust-sweeper, the Ewbank (she is still pre-vacuum cleaner, pre-telephone). The sideboard in the kitchen is a smeary scandal; a spider's web defines an angle of the sitting room ceiling; the glass door of the bureau cabinet is too dusty to reveal more than a murkiness of souvenir-shapes within. Outside, the lavatory latch won't hold, the yellow-painted door doesn't fit its frame, the cranky cistern leaks and there is need for a good dowsing with disinfectant. To step more than a few inches into the mildewed shed, tucked in between the WC and the kitchen wall, has long been imposs-ible: it is a congeries of garden tools useless now to Nana, coldly rotting furniture and other bric-a-brac largely pre-dating her arrival in the house and collectively exuding a sickly mustiness. A derisory strip of garden, contained in a brick bunker, runs across the back of the yard, and seems more apt for burying metal than propagating plants. There by the yard door is the metal 'ash bin', as she always calls it. All this, with a patch of sombre sky, would be her view if she turned to face the window; but she is hunched towards the electric fire as usual, and just now serving her daughter and grandson, with tea, biscuits and pomfret-cakes on her birthday, an advanced one, in early October, falling this year on a Wednesday – it's just like old times! The pot kept warm by a felt cosy goes far, for neither she nor her daughter can endure 'tea' with more than a modicum of actual tea in it, scented hot water, really. This weak tea is to him by definition 'ladies' tea', and perhaps Nana is a weak woman in some respects, though his mother isn't. The former is a bit weepy today, for this is the visit before he leaves home for university. 'I don't know, I don't know,' she repeats. 'I hope you'll not be getting ideas about staying down south.' He nibbles the miniature black discus of a pomfret-cake. 'I might,' he teases. 'Who knows?' She asks: 'Wouldn't you rather go some-where local? It's all a mystery to me. We never used to go away from home, excepting wartime. These days, I see, it's a different story. Well, you know what you want.' She sighs; and smiles. He looks down at the worn fireside carpet and notes the precise sound of a brandy-snap snapping. They are sad to leave.

21. When he next visited, she was frailer. 'I haven't a bit of use left in me,' she defiantly announced. 'Everything's a trouble, a *big* trouble.' She bade him take the triangular chocolate box out of the cupboard inside the collapsible dining table and he chose a ginger, his least favourite as a child. She said the other night she actually got lost in bed. Aware something was wrong, she

crawled from bedpost to bedpost and after a turmoil of search she found the light switch and, yes, she had been lying the wrong way round. 'Why go on, I want to know?' He was the more worried because he had read the Metaphysical poets and spotted a note to Donne's 'Nocturnall upon S. Lucies Day' pointing out that 'one of Hippocrates' signs of imminent death is when the sick man "makes the beds feet where the head should be"'. And yet it was as soothing as ever to sit with his grandmother; still the gentle register of her talk entranced him. He was under exam pressure, and tried to spend the following week in solitary study at his parents' house while they were away in the Lake District. When a dismaying, unexpected *frisson* of loneliness ran through him on the first afternoon, he sheepishly sought refuge at Nana's. He was glad to prolong his visit.

22. Then, of all things, she was forced to move house again. The demolition had begun in earnest of 'the Height triangle' of shops and streets in which she lived – no more resistance or prevarication was possible, two years of local petitioning proving in vain – and suddenly, improbably, she had something like a fresh start. Alas, she was not to flourish in New Herbert Street. Though the house, in a miners' terrace, brought some improvements – better plumbing, a street view, a telephone – and her health held up tolerably well, she hadn't been there a year before she took a fall on the steep, narrow stairs and hurt her hip. His last visit to a home of hers was terribly sad. Through the window he clearly saw her stir at his third ring. Tinier than ever, she seemed to collapse like one of her old loose-packed Christmas pillowcases as she inched towards the front door, admitting him at length. The door opened directly on to her living space – no hallway, and the only other downstairs room the kitchen. Her old face lit up to greet him. He kissed it. He

straight away regretted, as ever, his reluctance to call round, sinking readily into the amused, pampered passivity of a listener. 'Oh my old bones! I don't know what's to be done with me now!' she averred. Even the couple of yards to the front door were hard for her what with this hip, 'and that door gets heavier and heavier, believe you me!' They both huddled in front of the transplanted electric fire, though summer was not dead outside. She offered him the biscuit barrel, so familiar with its tightly fitting metal inner case and black knob on the lid. Ancient possessions such as the wide-brimmed pewter trophy inscribed to Grandpa in the 1930s and used as a dusty oranges and oddments bowl, the little black calendar, her plain plywood letter-rack, had faithfully followed her here, though they were beginning to have the air of stragglers. Her bits of furniture seemed tattier and more exiguous – the steadfast old bureau and grandfather clock had had to go. Yet she charged the room with her presence and with the atmosphere of the past. The tick-tocks may have stopped but the silence of her solitude would still normally be punctuated by the clacking of needles – those knuckly fingers managed to go on knitting. The kitchen cabinet, the crumb-infested utensils retained their distinctive greasy smell, preserving continuity. On they talked. He stayed longer than he had intended and wondered why he had to go even then. Why this endless leave-taking? She gave him one of her big unfaded smiles, but her eyes – so wide to see him, yet almost too poor to see him – were rinsed again in tears as she waved from the doorstep, staring through long time, until he turned the corner of the street.

23. Another fall, and this time she had to stay in hospital. The same side of the hip was damaged, and it refused to mend. They put her first in Hope, then Ladywell, then back in Hope – the

hospitals in this area are somewhat inopportunely named – when there really was no hope. Between the first two stints she had a last brief unhappy spell at home and at that time the dilemma of where she would best be accommodated became a burning one for her daughter. In the event she stayed in hospital wards. The almost daily visits grew physically and emotionally onerous to an unbearable degree for his mother. His visits, confined to the vacations, were infrequent enough to be positively interesting, for all the geriatric horrors he observed. Nana herself was more observer, initially, than bad case. She wryly outlined the elaborate arrangements necesary to speak with other patients in the ward. You had to get on your zimmer frame, set yourself creeping in the direction of the desired bed, and aim to pass it at the right moment to be noticed, only to find that you wouldn't be able to make yourself heard when you got there. She woefully pointed to the dreadful spectacle, in one of the Hope wards, of a lady nearly blind and deaf and in terminal pain who was pinioned to her chair by an eating tray, but rocked as far as she could backwards and forwards on her stomach to console herself as distressed children do, so Nana suggested. At one point the decrepit woman hysterically screamed: 'Take the board away! Take the board away!' But Nana had slipped into vagary and didn't seem to notice this shattering assault on the senses. Before he left her, she muttered something about pain, and he inquired, was she in any pain? 'Oh yes,' she replied blithely; but was strangely unconvincing.

24. Such a mood of flippant disconnectedness was increasingly her norm as she became wholly institutionalized and a slight Parkinsonism set in. She occupied her own room at Ladywell – Ladyill! – for nearly a year and dissolved by degrees into her own world of fantasticality. Conversations with her were hit-

and-miss: it was genuinely hard to know if she was with you or not, which was equally zany and distressing. She would blurt out the most surprising things: 'It's a shame, isn't it? And I always thought you were the perfect couple!' This, addressed to his mother, was a conviction that his parents had, belatedly, split up: perhaps a subterraneous wish-fulfilment, but oddly congruent in its Freudian way with some of his own dreams. Then, just as abruptly: 'The *TV Times* is always wrong these days!' Everything was 'a bit funny'. To a nurse who came in: 'If it wasn't for such as you there wouldn't be such as us.' Which had a superficial plausibility. She forgot everyone's name sooner or later, even her own daughter's, and her own. But Vera, she would airily scoff with what might be mistaken for sarcasm, 'is very good at remembering names. Everyone's good at something.' The thing that Nana had been good at all her life was knitting; now, after millions of stitches, she could no longer coordinate the needles, her hand was too twitchy, her eye too vague to get a needle-end, however thick, into a coil of wool, however slack. She didn't bother much with the magazines and library romances piled on the trolley-table beside her, on which perennially stood a Lucozade and a lavender bottle ('Lavender's blue, dilly dilly, Lavender's green'). She had given up on games of her favourite Patience. Television programmes blurred in her mind. She was a hapless, weary and confused old soul, but not yet gone. Intermittently she'd talk sensibly, recalling Grandpa in a clear sentence or two when drawn on the subject. He didn't venture the subject of the earlier husband, nor of the lost child. But one bright autumn afternoon, when she seemed unusually hale, propped up on three pillows with some colour in her cheeks, and had been making him laugh, he was emboldened to draw her on the subject of her 'future'. 'What do you think will actually happen to you?' he foolishly wondered. She paused, looked puzzled, and said plainly, 'I'm waiting to find out.' He persisted. 'But are you conscious of . . . of . . .?' Then broke off the question. Death, hers, had suddenly become a heartless reality. As he walked home along Eccles Old Road in the dusk he nonetheless felt braced by the audacity of such an intellectual dicing.

25. They went through her house before she died, his mother and he, on a winter's evening, knowing too well it was a terminal clear-out, that her days of private residence were over. He found the exercise not dispiriting, as though able to summon in advance some of that perversely elated energy that follows loss and pitches the bereaved into a fury of funeral arrangements; and also because, after all, his own mother's days were not numbered, he was not on the edge of an emotional precipice. But pathos filled the house like dust-motes; the fragility of her life was palpable – it powdered in the hand. Her possessions were not possessions now, they'd given her the slip. Perhaps only in his apprehension could such trifles as her letter-rack (never stuffed with letters), slim metal torch (for groping in the backyard at night), the scrap of ruled paper on which she had written her first telephone number in a faltering elderly hand (it lay in the flap of a handbag) retain a glimmer of meaning, and he filched them for souvenirs. His mother was no sentimentalist but she held on to some framed photographs and Grandpa's scrapbook. They rooted through cupboards, drawers and wardrobe, making piles of clothing, bedding and, alas, books for jumble. They started on cleaning the kitchen, igniting the whistly paraffin lamp to keep them warm. Rock music began thumping through one of the living-room walls. A young couple had, he remembered, moved in next door soon after Nana arrived, and it appalled him that the immemorial hush of her

homes must have been repeatedly thus violated: but the two of them agreed that she wouldn't have minded – her hearing was far too poor.

26. And she passed away. He was in London and received the news by phone from his father. It was a burden lifted from his poor mother. The funeral took place in the modest, modernist Height Methodist church on King Street in July. The church was spanking new, only seven years open, built on the site of a timber yard that had burned down. It was odd to hear his grandmother referred to by her full Christian name, as the young minister, who never knew her, repeatedly did. Just as her physical appearance was not, to his mind, eligible for comment, neither should she be conventionally named; she was too unique and near to him for that. She had, after all, eluded the telephone directory for most of her life. Now, though, she was a register item pure and simple. The short eulogy was touching – it really ought to have included something from Patience Strong. Aunty Vera wiped her eyes under her spectacles. The congregation was small but larger than expected, swollen by a few kind, sweetly scented old ladies who introduced themselves as the family filed solemnly out, to proceed in convoy to the cemetery.

27. He did not grieve unduly on that occasion because he had inordinately grieved for her while she was still alive. His mother did not seem particularly distraught either; her state was hard to gauge and he would not scrutinize her. In years to come she seldom voluntarily mentioned Nana: here was a difficult tale to tell, and best not begin. Who knows what was the cost of her long dying? Poignant feelings of guilt and embarrassment remained of Nana perhaps as memories of his flawless dignity and certain of his tomes survived of Grandpa. He himself rarely

talked about her and what she had meant to him. When, very occasionally, he was prodded on the subject of his fondness for her, he quickly noticed an ancient embarrassment gagging his reply; the same sort, doubtless, that tilted his mother firmly against taking the title 'Nana' when the first of her own grandchildren was born a few years later. The person as well as the sobriquet was curiously edited out of their family discourse; even the whereabouts of the headstone carved with her name in the cemetery was shamefully allowed to be lost. But by one route she was infallibly able to return into their midst. If ever somebody's tongue slipped on the word *precint*, there she'd irrepressibly be, slipping round again for morning coffee, slipping in through that missing letter *c*.

28. She survived from Gladstone's day to Thatcher's, indifferent to all prime ministers along the way, and for all her public role at the Methodist church pre-eminently living the private life. But the most private life can have its great moments. For him, the real moment of her death had come when he went with his mother to see her during the preceding Easter vacation at Hope Hospital in a new ward, her last, which they had considerable difficulty locating. Down one white anaesthetic corridor after another they trudged, passing the open doors of staff-rooms in which nonchalant nurses were having a fag; inadvertently exiting from the building at one point; retracing their steps until they they spotted the proper sign. Nana lay in an alcove in the middle of a spacious though not airy hall in the middle of a bed that seemed far too large for her: but it was she who had shrunk. Her face had changed terribly: all her teeth were out, she looked like somebody else; grotesquely mottled and old, a vagrancy of flesh; leering, smile-less. He stood at the foot of her bed aghast. His mother said something. Nana replied

feebly; her voice had sharply risen in pitch. He found he could not speak. Then he observed her wrists placed on the white sheet, her dear old thickly veined grandmotherly wrists, unchanged. A great quaking irresistible grief started up inside him. He could see no possibility of holding back tears, standing there at the foot of her bed. He hoped she'd not notice, but lucidly, with, indeed, an unutterable dignity, she asked his mother, 'Is he crying because of me?' That only made it harder to cope, as his mother struggled in embarrassment for a response. He controlled himself to the extent of kissing Nana goodbye and walking steadily out of the ward. He knew it was a goodbye to her for ever, and once in the corridor broke down. Staring blankly into the corner of a wall, his mother pausing for him, he howled, howled.

SIX

Involutes

prelude and fugue

Bronze by gold heard the hoofirons, steelyringing.

– James Joyce, 'The Sirens', *Ulysses*

. . . a chorus, &c., of elaborate harmony, displayed before me, as
in a piece of arras work, the whole of my past life – not as if
recalled by an act of memory, but as if present and incarnated in
the music: no longer painful to dwell upon: but the detail of its
incidents removed, or blended in some hazy abstraction; and its
passions exalted, spiritualized, and sublimed. All this was to be
had for five shillings.

– Thomas De Quincey, listening to music under the influence
of opium, *Confessions of an English Opium-Eater*

If all the world were paper

– Gustav Holst, double-fugue subject, *Fugal Concerto*

*The young Thomas De Quincey was attracted to William Words-
worth's poetry as by a 'deep deep magnet'. He considered himself
practically the poet's first admirer. Early he acquired (and eventually mislaid) a manuscript copy of Wordworth's unpublished
poem on the growth of his own mind, which would oddly, aptly,*

247

posthumously come to be known as The Prelude. *As a boy he wrote to Wordsworth at Grasmere and resisted the temptation to visit him there after absconding one midsummer dawn from Manchester Grammar School; embarrassment at his schoolboy condition held him back in pride. In his own miscellaneous and prolific writings – fourteen collected volumes of journalism, criticism, autobiography and visionary utterance – De Quincey often seems to be weaving the strands of something like a prose equivalent of* The Prelude, *examining the ways in which his mind, too, was formed by strangely resonant childhood experiences, which he finds recoverable not so much through the natural promptings of memory as by means of opium-heightened dreams, though these have to be of a certain quality ('he whose talk is of oxen, will probably dream of oxen'). Notorious in later life for the frankness of his brilliantly funny and insightful sketches of Wordsworth and his circle, De Quincey showed himself admirably able to break free from that sphere of magnetic influence. 'Put not your trust in the intellectual princes of your age; form no connections too close with any who live only in the atmosphere of admiration and praise,' he warned; while never closing his mind to Wordsworth's achievement nor failing to comprehend it deeply. Funny, exalted, experimental, centrifugal, his amazingly varied and fluent prose is, I think, the most fascinating of the English Romantic period.*

ONE

Thomas De Quincey, aged seven, illicitly enters the chamber where the dead body of his nine-year-old sister Elizabeth lies. It is noon. It is quiet. He stares, distraught, in the direction of the deathbed but sees only a wide-open window through which the Manchester sunshine is pouring in. A dry and cloudless, glorious day of death. The bed has been moved and its back turned to the door. He creeps over to look on the corpse, the angel face, which he doesn't cover with kisses, for he notes death's rapid work. He hears a wind. His trepidation changes into awe. The wind is solemn, mournful:

> Mournful! that is saying nothing. It was a wind that had swept the fields of mortality for a hundred centuries. Many times since, upon a summer day, when the sun is about the hottest, I have remarked the same wind arising and uttering the same hollow, solemn, Mnemonian but saintly swell: it is in this world the one sole audible symbol of eternity. And three times in my life I have happened to hear the same sound in the same circumstances, viz. when standing between an open window and a dead body on a summer day.

The abrupt glory of the day and abrupt frostiness of death, alternately, simultaneously apprehended, combine to set his mind reeling. In a trance he seems to see to the summit of the heavens and feels as if he is being billowed up there, up and infinitely up – to the throne of God, which recedes infinitely farther, just as a deathly wind keeps repelling his progress; until he is brought back down to the bedside and wakefulness. Next day he tries to visit Elizabeth again, but an autopsy has meanwhile taken place, the key in the locked door has been taken away. Thomas is shut out for ever:

> I have often been struck with the important truth – that far more of our deepest thoughts and feelings pass to us through perplexed combinations of concrete objects, pass to us as involutes (if I may coin that word) in compound experiences incapable of being disentangled, than ever reach us directly, and in their own abstract shapes.

Many a candlelit winter night at Greenhay – today's Moss Side – the pensive young De Quincey and his three sisters sat around the fireguard enthralled by stories from an illustrated nursery Bible which they ever implored their nurse to read to them and which not only inspired Thomas with a sense of religious grandeur but filled him with multiple images of summer. The sunlit landscapes of Syria, the disciples plucking the ears of corn, the very name of Palm Sunday – palms signifying the pomps of human triumph but equally the natural pomps of summer – such promises of warmth, light and abundance not only contrasted beguilingly with the gloom and flickering illuminations of the nursery but stood in blunt antagonism to that gloomiest of mortal tragedies as enacted in Jerusalem soon after Palm Sunday. From his re-imaginings of Scripture, death and summer were already mingled in his mind when he stepped into that deathly, summery, unlocked room:

> I have had occasion to remark . . . that the deaths of those whom we love, and indeed the contemplation of death generally, is (*cæteris paribus*) more affecting in summer than in any other season of the year. And the reasons are these three, I think: first, that the visible heavens in summer appear far higher, more distant, and (if such a solecism may be excused) more infinite . . . secondly, the light and the appearances of the declining and the setting sun are much more fitted to be types and characters of the Infinite; and, thirdly, (which is the main reason) the exuberant and riotous prodigality of life naturally forces the mind more powerfully upon the antagonist thought of death, and the wintry sterility of the grave. For it may be observed, generally, that wherever two thoughts stand related to each other by a law of antagonism . . . they are apt to suggest each other. On these accounts it is that I find it impossible to banish the thought of death when I am walking alone in the endless days of summer.

Another young child dead in the year's prime is Wordsworth's daughter Kate, on whom De Quincey has seriously doted. Leaving this world she finds a dwelling-place within his dream-world. He recounts in the *Confessions* a dream in which he stands at daybreak at the door of his Grasmere cottage beholding a mountain landscape familiar but magnified in scale and verdant beauty, devoid of living creatures but for cattle in the churchyard resting on Kate's grave. It is Easter Sunday and he steps abroad confident that the dewy peacefulness on this day of resurrection is to wash away his fevers and his fret. Instantly the landscape becomes starker, middle-eastern, with a distant prospect of the domes and cupolas of Scriptural Jerusalem. Enshaded by palms a child-woman sits raptly. Lost Ann, his companion from their days of destitution in London's Oxford Street seventeen years before, appears to him in pristine solemnity. At once vapours roll down from the mountains, darkness comes on and the scene changes a second time, to that very Oxford Street and those dark old days.

TWO

'The month was August, in which lay my own birthday; a festival to every thoughtful man suggesting solemn and often sigh-born thoughts,' De Quincey writes in the third section, 'The Vision of Sudden Death', of his greatest essay, *The English Mail-Coach*. He is travelling by night from Manchester to Westmorland along the Preston road perched on the box of the London and Glasgow mail next to the coachman. He is back in his native county of Lancashire in the middle of his life. He has taken a quantity of laudanum, having travelled two hundred and fifty miles northwards that day on a simple breakfast. The coachman seems to him Cyclopean, monstrous in size (but De Quincey is tiny), and monocular. Their departure from Manchester has been delayed by a wartime excess of foreign mails to be sorted – this is the Napoleonic era – giving De Quincey, a congenital procrastinator, cause to relish the fact that the post-office has never had to wait for *him*.

The configuration of circumstances is rare. De Quincey may be opium-shattered – since Oxford student days he has loved to enjoy his mental transports while thus in actual transport – but Cyclops is shattered by days of waiting to be summoned as a witness in a case being heard at Lancaster Assizes, drinking with companions as he waits and driving only in the depths of the night, consequently not sleeping in a bed for days and nights on end. He is apt to nod off. Soon he falls into impenetrable slumber. The guard, a tiresome and a tired songster, drops off too. De Quincey is left in sole charge of the hurtling vehicle. The seriousness of this lapse appears to be less than it is, for the busy Assizes, drawing people from across the county, is so demanding on horsepower that most of the animals are exhausted and out of commission by sunset, leaving night journeys abnormally tranquil. Not a wheel or hoof is to be heard besides their own. De Quincey ponders the scene. With his aptitude for paradox, his insight into the law of psychological antagonism which will make him so acute a literary critic, he finds the solemn stillness and natural beauty of the landscape, together with the sensed reposefulness of the sea decreasingly distant on their left, all the more soothing for a counter-impression of convulsive daytime transports sweeping back and forth to Lancaster, and the harsh recollection that here, in the industrial southern part of his native county, on a greater scale than anywhere on earth, past or present, human labour is being relentlessly expended and coerced (Peterloo is but a couple of

Augusts away). Yes, awareness of the sorrows of earth seems on such a night only an open sesame to the heavens. De Quincey is deep in reverie:

> The sea, the atmosphere, the light, bore an orchestral part in this universal lull. Moonlight, and the first timid tremblings of the dawn, were now blending; and the blendings were brought into a still more exquisite state of unity, by a slight silvery mist, motionless and dreamy, that covered the woods and fields, but with a veil of equable transparency.

He is close to the mid-point of his life, poised on the mail-coach on a fulcrum of before and after. He has published nothing; that is all to come, beginning with the big splash of the *Confessions* in 1821 which will be succeeded by nearly forty years of ripples. He is returning to the Lake District where he has a wife (they're not *quite* married yet) and baby boy, where he will presently, though improbably, edit the *Westmorland Gazette* for a year. In London he has, until recently, kept terms at the Middle Temple in a half-hearted pursuit of law, and has been arduously supervising the publication of a pamphlet, *The Convention of Cintra*, by his hero and difficult friend, Wordsworth, whose Grasmere cottage he has taken over. Since his late adolescence he has been plying between the north of England and the south. In Lancashire, in the silvery magic of this early summer dawn as the horses thunder on, it is to his Manchester childhood that his thoughts inevitably revert:

> 'Greenhay': – A country-house built by my father; and at the time of its foundation (say in 1791 or 1792) separated from the last outskirts of Manchester by an entire mile; but now, and for many a year, overtaken by the hasty strides of this great city, and long since (I presume) absorbed into its mighty uproar.

Quite. Father hardly lived there. No sooner had he built it than his tubercular condition impelled him to seek warm dry refuge abroad, preferably in places where he could prosecute the linen importing business of his Manchester firm. When he came home in 1793 – he was but forty – it was to die, giving Thomas his third experience of mortality only a year after Elizabeth's death, three years after that of his younger sister Jane: a series of premature deaths that continues throughout his long life. His rumbustious elder brother William, on whose side he reluctantly joins battle with mocking mill-boys twice daily as they traipse to and from their tutor's house in Salford, dies four years later at only fifteen years of age, having been relocated to a painter's studio in Hammersmith. Thomas's boyhood is now wholly subject to his mother's schemes and caprices. She is a strong-willed, high-toned, Evangelical but intellectual lady. It is she who, for some reason, at this point inserts the 'De' into the family name (how much less colourful our literary history would have been without it!), though she soon discards it for herself. She moves to Bath, where Thomas is put into Bath Grammar School, thence soon arbitrarily transplanted to a small private school in Wiltshire. In both establishments he impresses with his fluency in Latin and Greek; has, indeed, to underplay himself; but his mother is only the more fearful that he will succumb to pride. She sends him back up north, to taste the grit of the Manchester Grammar School.

Before following their mother to Bath, he and his comely younger brother 'Pink' had been boarded for a short time at the home of a friend and junior colleague of his father, John Kelsall, who is one of Thomas's guardians. It is a kind of Eden that Thomas tastes here, such as for him will always take the form of an encircling by sympathetic sisters. Kelsall and his wife are enjoying a newly married happiness which radiates throughout their household, all of whose members are young and include three female servants whom their mistress treats with uncommon courtesy and solicitude, as well as a two-year-old daughter. Thomas and his brother, respectively eleven and seven, are conveniently able to fill the gaps in the ascending scale of ages. Love and kindness reign; tempers do not fray; no rivalries, grudges, anxieties corrupt the family harmony. Thomas's are halcyon days:

> The spirit of hope and the spirit of peace . . . had, for their own enjoyment, united in a sisterly league to blow a solitary bubble of visionary happiness – and to sequester from the unresting hurricanes of life one solitary household of eight persons within a four months' lull, as if within some Arabian tent on some untrodden wilderness, withdrawn from human intrusion, or even from knowledge, by worlds of mist and vapour.

He basks in something of the same familial warmth – never quite forthcoming from his mother – while staying in Northamptonshire at Laxton, the grand house of a family friend, the young Lady Carbery, who treats him as an adult and inspires in him a more than sisterly affection. But these gains are knocked away by Manchester Grammar School. Here his conditions increasingly strike him as intolerable. He writes to his mother about the lack of opportunity for exercise or time to digest his food, about the air made unbreathable by factories, the unvarying routine, the general lack of liberty, amusement, stimulus. Manchester's unbridled commercialism interferes, he claims, with his Romantic visions. He has long outgrown the schoolboy milieu. Things are only made worse when the Lady Carbery set decamps temporarily to the area and Thomas is allowed to visit and amuse them in the evenings. He feels all the more trammelled after their departure. The intractability of his mother and guardians on the question of his going to Oxford early leaves nothing for it, he decides, but to run away. A generous sum arrives from Lady Carbery, to whom he has discreetly appealed for a loan, and he puts his plan into action. His flight will, of course, be made world-famous by the *Confessions*, particularly the expanded version of 1856 in which a thick layer of Manchester detail is added to a text mostly reticent about the names of people and places. But he is not to know that as he passes a sleepless final night in his familiar Long Millgate room and weeps – for all his antipathy to the school – weeps as he gazes at chair, table, hearth and picture in dawn-light, sure he will never gaze at them again; weeps simply for the year and a half of his past, which, happy or unhappy, dejected or occasionally hopeful and studded by private moments of intellectual release, suddenly appears to him as a totality, that is to say, as a figure of mortality.

THREE

Riding undisturbed – floating rather – through the beginnings of a summer dawn comparable to the cloudless one on which he made that early morning flit south-west to the bustling market town of Altrincham, again he sees his past coalescing into a whole, absorbing those eighteen months together with their aftermath in Chester and Wales, London and Oxford, and so much more – half a lifetime; and he ponders the moving, intricate ways of memory, how it gives and takes away, how it transforms what it touches. He is very attached to the Shake-spearean word *dislimn*. Faces soon begin to dislimn, even the face of a beloved infant in the mind of a bereaved mother; even, though he is reluctant to admit it, the features of his departed sister Elizabeth in his own mind. The Kelsalls' lulling family paradise, at the time perceived by De Quincey as wrapped around in protective shrouds of mist and vapour, like a cloud that has appropriately *dislimned*, lost its lineaments by degrees not just in the immediate recollections of young Thomas, once parted from it, but in actuality, as death or marriage claimed the servant girls, then death the mistress and child; the family's history furnishing a bleak allegory of the process of forgetting. Forgetting? More deeply considered, *is* there such a thing?

> Of this, at least I feel assured, that there is no such thing as *forgetting* possible to the human mind; a thousand accidents may, and will interpose a veil between our present consciousness and the secret inscriptions on the mind; accidents of the same sort will also rend away this veil; but alike, whether veiled or unveiled, the inscription remains for ever; just as the stars seem to withdraw before the common light of day, whereas, in fact, we all know that it is the light which is drawn over them as a veil – and that they are waiting to be revealed, when the obscuring daylight shall have withdrawn.

In the entrancing narcotic light of the imminent summer dawn, De Quincey cherishes his beautiful notion of the mind as palimpsest. Everything that happens which is of any significance can be re-limned if the mind is thrown into a sufficient convulsion, as by opium or in the grip of death. The whole pattern of your life can be thus instantaneously revealed to you, minutest details of your remotest experience recovered; as happened to his mother when she nearly drowned in a river at the age of nine (she has always insisted on the factual veracity of that incident, she is no romancer); or as repeatedly happens to De Quincey himself in the deep transports of his opium dreams. He fancies, very plausibly, that the fateful book of account with which Scripture awes us is nothing but the individual mind of each one of us. His speculations anticipate Freud's, even Derrida's. Dreams are man's conduit to the shadowy and infinite realm, but they are the key to the pysche. Not only is forgetting, in a sense, impossible but memory is an active agent, in the service of the psyche. In a letter to Wilhelm Fliess in 1896 Freud conceives of 'memory traces being subjected from time to time to a re-arrangement in accordance with fresh circumstances – to a retranscription'. De Quincey, too, knows that what *has* been may turn out to have been different:

> Even the character of your own absolute experience, past and gone, which (if anything in this world) you might surely answer for as sealed and settled for ever – even this you must submit to hold in suspense, as a thing conditional and contingent upon what is yet to come – liable to have its provisional character affirmed or reversed, according to new combinations into which it may enter with elements only yet perhaps in the earliest stages of development.

Time is not linear. It is epiphanic. It is the 'spots of time' which Wordsworth describes in his unpublished autobiographical poem. It is involutes. It is the prosperous merchant John Kelsall embosomed by the perfect family and at the same instant lurching along Manchester's main street an old wrecked man, bankrupted and alone, observed from a shop's doorway by the only other relic of that blessed household, Thomas De Quincey, who happens to be sheltering from the rain.

FOUR

Life is a dream. But no, it is not a dream. As the mailcoach hurtles on unguided across the sleeping county, and De Quincey's opium-sped thoughts fly faster and farther, endlessly searching yet self-involved, as though a fantastical fugue, life with its plethora of human accidents starts to exert a counter-force. Invisible as yet, but just audible to the Opium-Eater, is an approaching carriage; which realization horrifies him because, taking the benefit of a sandy surface to one side of the paved part of the road, the mailcoach is in the wrong lane, while, by reason of the same soft sand, the other vehicle is most unlikely to be. Collision is possible:

> I pretend to no presence of mind. On the contrary, my fear is, that I am miserably and shamefully deficient in that quality as regards action. The palsy of doubt hangs like some guilty weight of dark unfathomed remembrances upon my energies, when the signal is flying for *action*. But on the other hand, this accursed gift I have, as regards *thought*, that in the first step towards the possibility of a misfortune I see its total evolution: in the radix, I see too certainly and too instantly its entire expansion; in the first syllable of the dreadful sentence, I read already the last.

The mailcoach, built to publish national tidings imperiously through the land, is not at risk from any crash. De Quincey does not fear for himself; whatever kind of vehicle heaves into view, it will be perilously outclassed. Avoiding action falls upon him to take, and him only; for he knows he will be unable to scramble over the mailbags stacked on the roof to alert the sleeping guard to blow his horn, still less prise the reins from the marble grip of the comatose coachman. In his peculiar palsy he cannot act for thinking about the nature of action; he forgets what it is to shout. Suddenly the horses race round a sharp corner into a long dead-straight avenue which, with twin rows of lofty trees meeting overhead, resembles a Gothic cathedral aisle. At the far end a gig which looks as fragile as De Quincey feels is innocently advancing, seated inside it a courting couple, innocently courting disaster. Only a minute and a half, De Quincey estimates, remain to avert catastrophe, and it is *The Iliad* that comes to his aid. Achilles' war-cry pops into his classical mind; he emits a version of his own, to no avail; then another: to this the young man steering the gig responds. Now De Quincey the mover and shaker can do no more – but he spectates with burning assiduity. He considers the situation ethically: will the young man try to save the lady's skin as well as his own, and if not, will the loss of so craven a life be worth regretting? and then reckons the precise number of seconds available to the man – for he is not proving craven – in which to appraise the situation, reflect on it, pray for guidance, act. He considers the situation aesthetically, finding the young man's manifest courage *sublime*, and seeing in the maiden, who has been ripped from the romantic tenderness of a balmy and magical night into a raging confrontation with death, a true figure of tragic pathos. He considers the situation religiously, apocalyptically: the doomy countdown will surely leave the kissing couple sans shriving time before they meet their maker. But, wait, the man has got his horse to turn around. But they are not yet out of danger. The man must take at least another step to that end:

Hurry then, hurry! for the flying moments – *they* hurry! Oh, hurry, hurry, my brave young man! for the cruel hoofs of our

horses – *they* also hurry! Fast are the flying moments, faster are
the hoofs of our horses.

But slow the effect of De Quincey's talkative prose. Like a
cinematographer, he gives the suspenseful scene in lurid freeze-
frame. Frantic and frozen, the young man impels his horse on
to the crest of the road, which puts the front part of the carriage
out of the insensate mailcoach's path. But what about the rear?
De Quincey rattles out his television sports commentary even
as the vehicles pass and a collision occurs. The mail strikes the
off-wheel of the gig, leaving it immobilized and the young man
rigid with horror, and the gig seems to De Quincey, staring
behind him, to tremble like a human, and the lady's arms were
flailing in despair, the issue is uncertain. The mail turns a sharp
corner out of the avenue. The incident is over. But it passes in
its visionary direness permanently into the Opium-Eater's
dreams.

FIVE

'Action is transitory,' writes Wordsworth, but 'in the after-
vacancy/ We wonder at ourselves like men betrayed.' This
theatre of the interpenetration of summer and fatality forms
another *involute* (or the same), a Wordsworthian spot of time
but rendered by De Quincey's fine art through heightened
contrasts in an atmospheric, cinematic way very unlike the sober
meditations of *The Prelude*. Wordsworth's visionary moments
arise imperceptibly out of their surrounding ordinariness, but
De Quincey's are sealed off from the world of normality and
calm, as though a murder were about to be committed. That
knocking at the gate after Macbeth's murder of Duncan, on

which De Quincey composes a celebrated essay, is the subtle, barely noticeable but profound signal of return to normal life out of, as it were, an *involute*. Doubtless the mailcoach duly arrived at Preston that morning, Cyclops snoring himself awake, the guard resuming his sing-song unaware, and De Quincey enjoying a good breakfast after his journey; unless, of course, the whole episode has been a literary fantasy, an opium reverie. But either way it is into the realm of fantasy, by no means into the Wordsworthian light of common day, that the trappings of this particular involute are resumed and its implications worked out, *most tumultuously*, in a 'Dream-Fugue', which is De Quincey's boldest of prose experiments. The 'fourth movement' of *The English Mail-Coach*, this fugue follows rather precisely the specified musical pattern – what could be a more un-Wordsworthian enterprise? (actually it is Joycean, and the De Quincey parody in the 'Oxen of the Sun' episode of *Ulysses* focuses on this fugue) – as it transforms and magnifies imagery from the night-ride and the earlier symphonic sections of the essay into an apocalyptic phantasmagoria developing the theme of sudden death in its height, breadth and depth. Ships and seas and storms and quicksands, an infinite cathedral, vast sarcophagi covered with bas-reliefs provide the queasily altering backdrop. Summer reigns in glory, summer disappears; the mood is elated and it is despairing. The unknown lady from the Preston road appears on a pinnace with young revellers, who are wiped out by the advance of a warship from which the dreamer is observing them. Eventually he finds himself upon a triumphal equipage conveying news of the Waterloo victory, but threatening to crush a female infant in a frail, flower-strewn, misty carriage obliviously heading towards him along an immense cathedral aisle. Suddenly a bas-relief of a battle-torn Dying Trumpeter arises from the stone and with a threefold marble blast warns her of impending doom. Angels of life and death, perched beside her – she has grown to a woman now – upon the highest of high alabaster altars contend for her soul, and victory goes at last, at last, to the former. So De Quincey's pariah guilt at his inaction in the mailcoach is expiated. That unknown lady did not perish. Through the blessed infant-woman, archetype of all female figures precious to his soul, Kate Wordsworth, Ann from Oxford Street, sister Elizabeth are restored to him in a mighty final sentence re-running the fugue in a relieved *stretto* of desperate and cadential jubilation. But it is only a dream, a dream. The life of suffering goes on:

> . . . there is a mysterious sensibility connected with real suffering, which recoils from circumstantial rehearsal or delineation, as from violation offered to something sacred, and which is, or should be, dedicated to privacy. Grief does not parade its pangs, nor the anguish of despairing hunger willingly count again its groans or its humiliations. Hence it was that Ledyard, the traveller, speaking of his Russian experiences, used to say that some of his miseries were such that he never *would* reveal them.

De Quincey's long life, seventy-five years of it, an astonishing span for one so racked by opium, is not a dream, though it often resembles a fugue, in the word's secondary sense as flight, escape from customary surroundings. His flights, in the later years, are invariably from creditors. Along with his illnesses and premature deaths among those nearest to him, intractable debts chequer his days in relentless, wan chronology. The guard's horn in *The English Mail-Coach*, which De Quincey in his crisis could not stir himself to seize and which mutates felicitously in the 'Dream-Fugue' into the stony instrument of the Dying Trumpeter, is a motif undergoing further but droll metamorphosis in De Quincey's life. A beleaguered, reclusive scribbler for years in Edinburgh (where he is buried), most maverick of family men, desperately trying to keep up appearances while falling apart, he is regularly 'put to the horn'; which is to say, three blasts sounding in the market-place to signify not that De Quincey is a debtor – as such he cannot be imprisoned under Scottish law – but, fantastically, that he has disobeyed a specially obtained royal command to settle his debt in the name of the crown and can therefore be gaoled as a traitor! He flits from one dismal rented room to another, leaving the rent unpaid and precious papers behind, forgetting what has been left where. One 14 August 1832 he has to abscond at five in the morning, suspecting that his editor Blackwood has let the secret of his current whereabouts slip. In all, he spends his declining years barely afloat on a sea of manuscript, while undergoing a sea-change into Text – into the Boston collected edition, then Hogg's. He has sons, daughters and a wife to rescue him from his papers and his papers from him. But suddenly three of the sons, including his first-born, are dead. Margaret, his wife, passes away in 1837, to become for him another female symbol of lost paradise, recoverable amid the organ tones of the mighty fugue. His doughty mother in her late nineties predeceases him by only thirteen years. Out of a pastel drawing of himself, two daughters and a granddaughter made in 1855, he peers uncannily down the generations at one; quizzical, almost smiling, a child-man with a large head and in a jacket far too big for him. He has lived decently, honourably, if dreadfully poor at honouring his monetary debts. He has endured more physical and mental pain, he knows, than he ever *would* say; though he has made suffering his theme. *Suspiria de Profundis*: sighs from the depths, sighs *form* the depths. The profoundest suffering is the earliest and the earliest inscription on the manuscript of the mind is suffering:

In the illustration imagined by myself, from the case of some individual palimpsest, the Grecian tragedy had seemed to be displaced, but was *not* displaced, by the monkish legend; and the monkish legend had seemed to be displaced, but was *not* displaced, by the knightly romance. In some potent convulsion of the system, all wheels back into its earliest elementary stage. The bewildering romance, light tarnished with darkness, the semi-fabulous legend, truth celestial mixed with human falsehoods, these fade even of themselves as life advances. The romance has perished that the young man adored. The legend has gone that deluded the boy. But the deep deep tragedies of infancy, as when the child's hands were unlinked for ever from his mother's neck, or his lips for ever from his sister's kisses, these remain lurking below all, and these lurk to the last.

Once again Thomas Quincey, aged seven, enters the chamber where the dead body of his sister Elizabeth lies. It is noon. It is quiet. He stares, distraught, in the direction of the deathbed but sees only a wide-open window through which the Manchester sun is shining.

Inventory of a Shed

Even now there are places where a thought might grow

– Derek Mahon

Sits tranquilly on its concrete plot illegally preserving pure asbestos walls. Mossy roof tiles. Heavy wooden eaves. Windows and floorboards from the old garage.

Creak round the stiff wooden door-fastener, unstick the door from its frame and sniff! A cool wooden smell, sawdusty, damp, welcoming, musty, anciently familiar. Private but not secretive place. Its contents start to come at you. What have we here?

A 'Sudbury Soil Tester' – oblong carton on a ledge. Large packets of 'Rose Plus', 'Phostrogen', which is soluble lawn food, 'Perfect Plant', which is leafshine. Easily nameable items for a start.

That tall thick sinuous turquoise vase, whose turning on the potter's wheel I can imagine – it keeps so much freshness. But it has been abandoned – a tall middle-aged lady, still shapely, on the shelf.

A garden rake. Shears for privets. Long wooden-handled spades, planed by years of my father's grip. Hand-trowel. Old serrated hosepipe. Old faithful.

A rusted tin of rusty screws and nails. Boxwood ruler marked in inches, its jointed limbs folding with a clack, glued by the tip of a nail.

Wooden tennis rackets, boxes of greeny used balls (a childhood passed to the thock of tennis). Tennis trophies old and recent – engraved metal cups or shiny plastic figurines on wooden pedestals.

A box of clothes-pegs, mostly plastic, the odd wooden manikin hanging in there. Nests of plastic plant-pots, the odd earthen-ware pot hanging in there.

A toy pistol with machine-gun rattle dropped on the rough-planked floor. Chad Valley slide projector in a box of toys. A skipping-rope. A clothes-line.

Folding aluminium and canvas chairs, a folding aluminium and canvas sun-bed. No deckchairs, I'm afraid, any more.

A red plastic watering 'can'. A used-up can of paint, with glazed white crust on the bottom.

A dilapidated red handbrush, the paint chipped, the clumps of bristle terribly thinned, worn out as an old dog.

Cardboard box of Christmas decorations – wan reminiscences of the glittering delights they have brought and may yet bring; when they are not lights but *delights* indeed; while now they are merely little orbs and ovals of crudely coloured glass, tinsel exposed as a sham.

My old plankton-net with its small square hard metal frame for shoving into pond-bed with collector's ruthlessness.

Antiquated kitchen-scales and weights painted a ludicrous cream, the bulky weights marked of course in pounds (lb) and ounces (oz).

Blackened iron mincing-machine with bell like a saxophone's and hand-crank as of an early gramophone and clamp for attaching it to the kitchen table while you made your mincing music. Childhood delusion: mincemeat is not meat but a kind of jam.

Those pharmacist's exact scales I acquired during a fad for chemistry: fine-curved copper trays each held in an inverted V-shape on a cord, as in the constellation Libra. Flat chipped wooden box and tarnished rag for the thing and its delicate weights.

Prismatic army compass, a thick round block, screw on the side (for what?), wobbling dial, perspex missing from the metal lid. You screw your eye against the pencil-line of the upright prism and descry degrees of orientation, acquire the magnetic truth of things! But it never worked.

A coffee table's fawn's legs dangling from the rafters.

Cheapjack kitchen cabinet with yellow painted door, containing what? I have to shift some boxes and a suitcase to find out. A couple of framed photographs, a book of Mazas's violin studies, Beethoven's Rondo in C, a red paperback of Christmas carols, a battered hard-covered collection of community songs, a pile of school magazines. *Progress Papers* for swotting at home. A rolled up, wide-angled Pendleton High School photograph of 1946 with my mother in it somewhere. From one of the framed photos my mother's own mother starts back into life with such forceful realism I recoil. I'd really forgotten what she looked like! But her features are, I suppose, part of me and the way I see the world.

My butterfly storebox. Pale plywood. Inside a few tatty moths – Yellow Underwings mostly – and a smell of camphor.

On the floorboards evidence remaining even now of the ingrained droppings of that poor rabbit and guinea-pig whose hutches we children so reluctantly and ineptly cleaned on Saturdays. *Saturdays!*

On the floor beneath a low shed-length shelf which my father has oddly installed, a pile of his *Practical Householder* magazines going back years.

Some of the old books have gone, a quaint, immensely detailed 1950s *Home Cyclopaedia*, for example. But here are several of the small oxblood volumes (undated) of that improving series published by Odham's with titles – embossed in a little rectangle on the hard cover – such as *How to Write, Think and Speak Correctly, The Home Counsellor, The Wonderful Story of the Human Body*. I flick through *Real Life Problems and Their Solution*, remarking the Enid Blytonish idealist illustrations and section-headings like 'Should "Weak" Boys Go In For Athletics?', 'Can "Art" Photographs Contaminate?', 'How Should I Treat A Young Bookworm?' Not, though, 'How Should I Write An Autobiography Of True Contingency?'

It's so easy to peek into the shed and see nothing. But even then you find you have received impressions, even of utmost ordinariness. How beautiful mediocrity can be in hindsight!

That ineffably ordinary table lamp, tapering cheap white porcelain zig-zagged in faint gold – even here memory may work its alchemy. By its metaphorical light you find you can suddenly see plenty. The unlikely survival of such a nondescript object illuminates days of ordinariness that were, that *are*, our existence: what we have.

A cribbage-board. An old wooden box of dominoes, empty. An unstoppered Thermos revealing its vulnerable silvered glass insides.

Each new glimpse at these shed things seems to arouse vibrations, as though the objects themselves were soliciting our attention. But it is rather we who need them; *I* who need that lamp, lump of the past.

Kim's Game. In the garden after a casual glimpse or two at the shed, how many of its contents can I list? Well, start with the electric lawn mower . . .

For all its changeableness – and objects are being constantly thrown away and added – the glimpsed shed is more stable than the glimpser, led hither and thither by life, though both will vanish in due course. The glimpser's psychological identity is confused by all this wandering into the before. The problems of his present may seem to be assuaged by this curious contact, but definite existential danger is incurred. He reels. *I* reel.

Fruiterer's crates standing end-on as shelves. A packing case for house removal – yet we've never removed.

Front door keys secreted on a bed of dust behind a curtain of cobwebs in an angle of the rafters. If I return to the house late (tipsy) I must fumble in darkness for them. Then the shed is truly cave-like, its objects a generalized mystery, equally dark and shed-like. The back-garden, black or moonlit, is another and greater mystery. That sheer being there. Unsayable.

Inventory of a Shed

And in the light of morning the keys are replaced. The shed, musty and cool, seems dull, reassuring. My mind's elsewhere. But a thought starts to grow, seeded by some nugatoriness catching my eye: the thought that my life-story could begin from any one of these jumbled but actually all too significant objects – a wooden clothes-peg, if you like – and expand by endless association into volumes, and the telling would never be done. I'm fascinated yet repelled by the idea. For once embarked on the task, I would be unable to go on properly living, immobilized like Borges's Funes by the world's infinite minu-tiae, the fatal specifics of memory; living embodiment of the death of invention.

271

Two Poems

Garden Centre

Cacti. Their endless alert sleep purifies outwards. They spread tranquillity and cajole me into loving my best things and best places, and conjure up my mother's garden and her trips to garden centres; though my mother dislikes cacti.

When I step into the heightened world of the cactus-room, and touch its glass, its palpable heat, its arid soil, I know my childhood as some Buddha-lands, the sweet suffusion of a great composure; prickly though it was.

And there's my mother gathering plants.

A Riddle

a. They were hard manuscripts to copy and few people could do justice to them. Schlemmer lived in the Graben, not far from the Kohlmarkt, in the rear part of a house. He had trained assistants, in particular one who worked for him for many years and, my mother told me, made his copies in a dark nailmaker's arch under the entrance gate to the Fischhof (then the Galvagnihof) on the Hoher Markt.

b. Before becoming a travelling salesman for Muldivo, my father held down a job at Lisberg's, dogsbody for both the father and the son. From a back window of the gloomy office facing Broughton's Upper Camp Street, he could observe the dark little workshop in an arch where the solution was made for waterproofing the items, the military-style white macintoshes, for instance. He ferried the father and son about the war-torn city and already knew the ways of gasket and distributor well. They gave him a good but scarcely effusive reference, misspelling conscientious. That was before the 'cold canvassing' began.

'Salford Toccata'

But he is come in cold-as-workhouse weather
Poor as a Salford child.

– John Short, 'Carol'

... Manchester on the south side of the Irwell standeth in
Salfordshire ...

– John Leland, *Itinerary*, 1538

Manchester and Salford

There's a brass-band piece by Harrison Birtwistle called *Salford Toccata* because it was commissioned by the Salford College of Technology, where it was premièred by college players conducted by Elgar Howarth in 1989. A chunky, complex, brightly spluttering piece, with just a hint of that cornettish northern melancholy endemic to brass bands, it isn't a toccata in an overly Scarlatti-ish and speedy sense of the word (though Birtwistle has written far less plausible movements under such a designation) but it *is* Salford's; or, as the Radio 3 presenter announced it, *Sorl-ford's*. That is so very unlikely and touching.

You remember being touched to learn that Salford was to have its own festival in the summer of 1980, the 750th anniversary of the granting of its first charter, for it had never occurred to you that your home city was in the running for such a many-splendoured, middle-class thing. Harrogate, Henley, York and Bath yes, but not sombre Salford, capital city of grime and grind, the 'classic slum' of Robert Roberts's eponymous study. It wasn't a dazzling affair. The attractions were predictable festival-hoppers like Paco Peña, Humphrey Lyttelton, Georgie Fame. In fact it was largely a local sports and fishing festival. But at least Salford was trying. It reminded you of the time in your childhood when you formed stamp- or card-collecting clubs or held jumble sales at your gatepost, so desperately wanting to be taken seriously, yet knowing all along you were just a boy with baubles.

Manchester might well have held a festival, Manchester did grown-up things. It was the big city, it was 'town', Salford standing to it ever in a role of reluctant dependency. Salford councillors repeatedly found that their plans were inextricably involved with those of their opposite numbers on the other side of the Irwell, complaining they were 'like little children waiting for the commands of their parents, as if they could not stir a step without Manchester'.[1]

Manchester (1)

The relationship between the cities on the Irwell is ticklish. Salford, as it never forgets, is also senior to Manchester, having been created a manor or 'hundred' as far back as 919, and been inventoried in 1086 in the Domesday Book ('there are many hays and a hawk's aery there'), in which year Manchester was created a mere subsidiary manor under Salford's administrative jurisdiction. On the other hand, Salford, lacking a church, had to be part of the parish of Manchester, which boasted St Mary's, the Manchester Cathedral to be. Salford was granted a charter (by Ranulph, Earl of Chester) in 1230 but Manchester did not get one (from its baron, Thomas Grelley) until 1301 and was not properly consituted as a free borough until 1846.

Old rivalries persist. Salfordians point out with a sort of battered pride that Manchester Docks were really in Salford, that the first municipal free library, public swimming baths, gas street-lighting, technical college, sanatorium and even the first smoke-free zone were Salford achievements, decidedly stealing a march on its 'twin' city. The balance is somewhat redressed now that the docks have become a smart leisure, business and residential complex, neatly post-modern in design, known as Salford Quays.

But no one quite credits the twinship notion: there has never been enough physical equality and compatibility for that to ring true. Manchester is undeniably great. Salford, for all that it has seen rows of millionaire's mansions as well as slums, is apt to be set down for beggarly if not base. Salfordian self-vaunting has the rueful defensiveness of the imperialist-exploited, in which lurks the recognition that to achieve anything at all is something in Salford. Bottom of the heap is where the Salfordian secretly thinks to belong; his pride is largely kickback (though this can be of an oddly empowering kind). The Manchester and Salford relationship is the eternally English one of class-status and embarrassment. As long as there's a Manchester it will be embarrassing for Salford to be merely Salfordian, an embarrassment figuring that of north–south English encounters in general.

How awful, in one's perception of people's perception of things, to have had to settle for SGS (Salford Grammar School) when there was an *MGS*! Such consanguinity as there is between the cities serves mainly to permit the Salfordian to

claim to the wider world, almost truthfully, that he or she is
'from Manchester'.

Salford (1)

We are all to some extent embarrassed by our origins, whose
awkward particularity we spend our lives, *make* our lives,
seeking to validate one way or the other; but what if your
origins really *are* embarrassing, famed as a 'classic slum'? Given
thus to feel in your bones that you stand at the *ne plus ultra* of
mediocrity, you will answer contingency with contingency.
You'll want to touch Salford only at certain points and only let
it touch you lightly. There's a Salford you badly, with your
battered pride, want to give its due and a Salford you don't
want at all. You don't want the extreme abrasiveness of accents,
the yobbish angry stares at bus-stops, the murderous behaviour
of crack-dealers and football supporters, the Salford that is the
object of sociological enquiry and written up in the *Guardian*:
the world of the Ordsall Estate.

You want the Salford that is . . . *what*? The Salford that has
become for you a beautiful idea. This you jealously reserve for
your own use. When you recently overheard someone in a
London café mentioning the place, you felt a proprietorial
chagrin. Paradoxically, the beautiful idea is in essence one of
profound decency, *normality*. Often you don't really believe the
other Salford exists.

Salford and Manchester

*Salford is a large town legally distinguished from Manchester for
parliamentary purposes, and divided from it physically by a river,
but else virtually, as regards intercourse and reciprocal influence, is
a quarter of Manchester; in fact, holding the same relation to*

Manchester that Southwark does to London; or, if the reader insists upon having a classical illustration of the case, the same relation that in ancient days Argos did to Mycenae. An invitation to dinner given by the public herald of Argos could be heard to the centre of Mycenae, and by a gourmand, if the dinner promised to be specially good, in the remoter suburb.[2]

Swinton Park Road

You have not left home once and for all, your escape is tenuous, you find you have to touch base, as they say, fairly often. Flitting back and forth, north and south, you see things from your peculiar changing perspective. Re-immersed in the old life you easily recover its awkwardnesses. Then returning south, you rapidly find that the complex, intense, difficult but real experience which was being at home, being in Salford, has again been transformed into a primarily aesthetic one. What was opaque becomes readily knowable, what was embarrassing the foundation of a literary sort of inquiry. One day, perhaps, when you have inquired enough, you will break from your childhood with a deep true severance.

Irlams o' th' Height (1)

Of the 'Height' village of your childhood, swept away to create an enormous traffic clearway, only three buildings survive – two stoutly made pubs, the Red Lion and half-timbered Dog and Partridge, unchanged, of course, in function and not very much in outward appearance; and Barclays Bank, an odd but quaint two-storey construction, with a blunt, white, slightly jutting ground floor and an upper part featuring a pair of pointed gables, narrow windows and a chimney-stack prominent at either side of the steep little roof. The building began life as a

278

police station – the larger gable is carved with the city coat of arms and *Integrity and Industry* motto – but throughout your early youth it was for you a sanctuary of stationery.

Pens in holders, stamps and inkpads, trays and boxes, printed forms, cheque-books, receipt-books, ledgers, paper galore, all in circulation and the more compelling for that, made this a stimulus to rival or possibly surpass that of the stationery department at Lewis's in town, where the pens and pencils were fixed behind glass, or even that of your primary school head-master's cramped office, riding high upon whose alluring clutter was a set of three tall handsome quill-like pens which soared out of their holders as though on wings and, on the two or three times you were able to glimpse them, held you with an almost erotic fascination.

The bank's distinctive gentle odour of paperwork and polish – that of the weighty wooden counter – you caught instantly on passing through the double doors; and no sooner inside than you had a sense, too, of being at the heart of the local community. Politeness reigned; the place and its civic values seemed as impregnable, indeed, as a police-station, though no one would have thought the phenomenon worth remarking.

For years after the road developments threw up a 'Shopping Giant', the bank stood alone, fulfilling the same role as before, preserving its civilized odour, but looking outwardly as implausible as a gingerbread cottage in a concrete jungle. The national mores changed. Shoppers went about in fear, knowing their infants might be abducted in the middle of the crowded precincts, knowing they themselves might be shot at inside or outside a bank. Wasn't your own father witness to a quiet hold-up in this so very inviolable Barclays?

Well, there's no reason why a bank should have to double as an anti-social centre indefinitely and Barclays finally pulled out of the Height. Now a discount furniture business has filled every square inch of the banking hall with dismal lumber, square inches on to which it had been criminal to trespass. You notice that the new owner has thought fit to install a few more bars on windows and door.

And is it merely sentimental to bemoan the replacement of that dignified place with this cheapjackery? Most buildings (apart from pubs) change their function with time (banks sometimes change into pubs). Whatever was built can be rebuilt. There is a cycle of ruin and restoration that governs our civic environment. True, your childhood mornings in the bank cannot return or really be recycled. But aren't they better as fond memories than continuing, wearying habits? Shouldn't one 'give over' all the fussing, the nonsense, 'live in the present'?

'No, no,' you protest. 'Don't ask me to live in the tawdry present. Anything, please, but that!'

Broughton

Lowry's pencil drawing, *Houses in Broughton*, of 1937, is a telling expression of his genius for Salford. How he captures the pallor of the northern city, not merely when it is under snow, but in its daily being, under its familiar sky! Yet this *is* a special day, snow lies thickly all around, the blackened stereotype of the city is annulled. A wind blows with modest force across the picture from left to right, bending the higher-up of the leafless trees and giving direction to the smudge of chimney smoke at the end of the terrace behind the rear mound.

These are five ordinary houses, they do not have the derelict grandeur investing so many of his house portraits; they are quotidian Broughton on a day, however, of snow. Pressed into the snow is – Lowry's pencil! which amputates some of the feet of those children and dogs who are glad of the town's deliverance for these brief white hours. But though there is a sinking into the snow – of things with wheels, long thin things, boxy Broughton things left out on the waste ground the night before – the counterforce of the picture is to thrust things up: the stakes of the clumsy, well-meaning fence occupying the foreground, the receding railings, the signposts, a telegraph pole, the blunt irregular protruberances of a building or buildings otherwise concealed, the waving wispy branches of the trees and waving arms of a little girl. The true subject of the drawing lies between these upward and downward impulses in the tender amplitude of the crisp snowy contours, a generosity of surface which invites you to participate in it, give yourself to it, return home to it, as though in a state of relief after years in a far country. It is a version of home neither cloying nor delusory. It does not, like an all too vivid photograph of an actual scene from your past, leave you lost in wonderment and debarred from entry: you *can* come in here. Nor is there the connotation of a regressive escape from present reality. In its image of abiding calm mundanity, fresh and glowing slightly, the drawing strikes an attitude to life which only increases your appetite for life; and this in a way which is at one with the medium itself. The drawing has the easeful yet acute, intimate yet provisional character that is the way of pencil.

'I'm immensely fond of pencil,' the artist said. 'I like pencil to hang up in my house.'[3]

Light Oaks Park

The peeling bark of these silver birches isn't an evocation of your childhood, but the thing itself, the very selfsame flaking brittle silvery knobbled bark. Touch it.

You have only to turn your head, much less alter the direction of your stroll, and the park, the world, seem profoundly different. The cool green contours describe you.

Each time alone in the park is a sounding into your self, an appraisal of your history to this point. You have got this far.

*

Chat Moss

From here, on the road to Manchester, we passed the great bog called Chatmos, the first of that kind that we see in England, from any of the south parts hither. It extends on the left-hand of the road for five or six miles east and west, and they told us it was, in some places, seven or eight miles from north to south. The nature of these mosses, for we found there are many of them in this country, is this, and you will take this for a description of all the rest. The surface, at a distance, looks black and dirty, and is indeed frightful to think of, for it will bear neither horse or man, unless it is an exceeding dry season, and then not so as to be passable, or that any one should travel over them. What nature meant by such a useless production, 'tis hard to imagine, but the land is entirely waste, except for the poor cottagers' fuel, and the quantity used for that is very small.

From hence we came on to Manchester, one of the greatest, if not really the greatest mere village in England. It is neither a walled town, city, or corporation; they send no members to Parliament; and the highest magistrate they have is a constable or headborough; and yet it has a collegiate church, several parishes, takes up a large space of ground, and, including the suburbs, or that part of the town called [Salford] over the bridge, it is said to contain above 50,000 people.[4]

Barton

Your favourite balloons in childhood – nothing touched them – were those fixed to a purply brick tower standing in the middle of the ship canal at Barton, great earth-coloured, leathery orbs of cane which rose gradually, impressively when the liners were approaching and the iron aqueduct, bearing the ferrous Bridge-water Canal, and arched iron roadbrige had alike to swing. The swinging capacity was an engineering marvel of its day, but though the stately, gigantic, clangorous movements filled you with awe, and the passage of the ship through the narrow channel was always as majestic as it was surprising (just as the distant sight of an ocean liner cleaving through the level Lancashire fields was both solemn and surreal), it was the balloons that gave the subtler fillip.

You looked for them whenever your father was mooded to take you to explore Barton aerodrome and the duckboard pathways of the canal bank, or through the windows of his car when, driving to or from Davyhulme, you would be 'bridged', and have to wait in line with impatient motorists, yourself quite happy to wait. Once you spotted them during a primary-school boat trip along the canal's whole length, thirty-seven miles from Salford Docks to Liverpool then back, a memorably long day, whose curious triumph was your success in faking an afternoon nap. Even being the best at falling asleep conferred a status then. Not many months after you re-opened your eyes, it must have been, when the balloons disappeared. Of course, as true balloons they should have floated to the heavens; but you were convinced that they fell, strange heavy fruits, plop, into the oily waters.

Seedley

You heard of so many Manchester districts – neighbourhoods, wards, boroughs, towns, cities, villages, metropolitan counties – their place-names so intimately familiar, yet in a way that was by no means tantamount to exact geographical knowledge. Could you confidently say on what points of the compass lay Oldham, Bolton, Rochdale in relation to home? Precisely where, within the limits of Salford, were Little Bolton, New Windsor or Wallness to be found? What were the significant differences between Pendle*ton* and Pendle*bury*? Where did Seedley begin and end? The names alone carried the burden of the place's being.

Seedley, for instance, couldn't help seeming *seedy*, and indeed was. Seedley was *Salfordly*, local to a painful point of embarrassment. Odd to think the ward nurtured the likes of James Agate and Alistair Cooke, local boys far from localized in their professions – the former the voice of dramatic criticism in the *Sunday Times* for twenty-four years; the latter after half a century still the true voice of Anglo-America on the airwaves.

Peel Park

Wordsworth wrote a famous poem about a leech-gatherer. Sir Kenneth Clark compared L.S. Lowry to a leech-gatherer. On the ground-floor of the Lowry gallery at Peel Park, Salford, a simulated 'historical' street, Lark Hill Place, has been assembled to trace back Salford life through the three centuries, and next to the door of one little address is a gilt plaque advertising the services of a 'bleeder with leeches'. She was your great-grandmother (she also ran a tiny pub). Your father unearthed this plaque from his mother's cellar. Now a German couple have noticed it. The woman is meticulously pronouncing the name and trade with a certain incredulity, which the man and you yourself share. You wonder whether leeches were more easily obtained in those days than when, a half century or so earlier, Wordsworth's 'decrepit Man' found they had 'dwindled long by slow decay', persevering in his quest across the weary moor.

Pendlebury

You lived in Pendlebury until you were one and a half, near the rugby league ground, the covered market and the immense church of St Augustine. Once or twice you were taken back to the area by your mother and visited the market. You had an obscure sense of affiliation or obligation, but were jolly glad you'd moved away. It was picturesque, busy, coarse, it was not home. You'd patrol the tatty stalls and rise above them, though eager to buy things – toys, books, stationery, comics, sweets, ice-creams, anything. You'd notice the dirt-ingrained faces of the hard selling-women, the sleaziness of the men, the urchin boys you'd hardly want to play with. The vending cries contin-uously emitted were cutting as the blades of aproned butchers in their sawdust-dry and blood-moist booths.

Was this your true parade? It was an expedition all the same, a complicated bus route then an uphill walk; strange smells; at one point, through the vacancy in a derelict terrace, an unpre-cendented view of Manchester (your tutelage). A childhood passes getting on and off the bus and walking to the doctor or the dentist or a different market.

At Pendlebury Market once the two of you met a lady of your mother's age though looking older and exotic, off-puttingly, speciously so. She was gipsy-like, shawled, with jewels of paste, of sawdust, yet shy and softly spoken. Her son was perhaps a day older than you yourself, which made him altogether senior. He too had a flavour of down at heel, felt foreign, Jewish and rough. He mixed, you knew, with wicked boys, an accomplice in intimidation, but remained somehow as shy as his mother. When you were stopped by his gang on the way home from school – that fearsome hill, that alleyway! – he could mitigate or even remit the punishment, saying 'Leave him alone, he's my cousin!'

Charlestown

That day, when you went a short apprehensive distance down Broughton Road from Pendleton Church to work on a lower sixth-form history essay about the American Wars of Independence in the little Charlestown Library, a prefabricated, vestigially L-shaped, green-painted shack, quaint in a dull sort of way, where you'd never been before. Here you found the book you needed and a table on which to complete your essay, which you wrote on fresh foolscap sheets ruled in faint green feint. The quiet pleasantness of the morning became the pleasantness of finishing your work.

You left for lunch at your grandmother's house up in Salford 6, where your mother was also going to be. But in memory it seems as though the house were located somewhere in the unfamiliar, perhaps dangerous depths of the city, towards which you had been heading, rather than where it actually was, that little safe street soon to be demolished, soon to be transposed, in any case, into the complex, wide space of your imagination.

Little Mr G., the nervous but plucky history master, singled out your essay for praise. Today you're back on site, at the top of Broughton Road, descending towards the library, which survives. A rather strangely idyllic memory.

Barr Hill

For once you are actually walking along this far stretch of Bolton Road, not dreaming of it. It seems more rather than less hallucinatory. The gates and lodge-houses at the junction with Chaseley Road are startlingly real, or do you mean unreal? At the bus-stop by your erstwhile – very erstwhile – barber's you feel bewildered, though the destination-board on a bus bound for Westhoughton, Blackrod and Chorley rouses your topographical imagination momently.

The area is for you, if queerly, a laboratory of time and fascination as you lean against the bus-stop uneasy in the sunshine of an ordinary afternoon, your dreams entwined with your reality; though for the youth on his bike darting to and from Barr Hill, in and out of the little concourse of that garage being rebuilt there, everything couldn't be more normal.

Kids though! Schoolkids lolling with their fags *inside* the entrance hall of your old school building – they have no need for the rusted bikesheds. In terraced houses on the opposite side of Dronfield Road are the sideboards, vases and lace curtains of front parlours. Some classic examples still survive. Widows haunt them.

*

Cross Lane (1)

All Salford is built in courts or narrow lanes, so narrow that they remind me of the narrowest I have ever seen, the little lanes of

Genoa. The average construction of Salford is in this respect much worse than that of Manchester, and so, too, in respect to cleanliness. If, in Manchester, the police force, from time to time, every six or ten years, makes a raid upon the working people's districts, closes the worst dwellings, and causes the filthiest spots in these Augean stables to be cleansed, in Salford it seems to have done absolutely nothing. The narrow side lanes and courts of Chapel Street, Greengate, and Gravel Lane have certainly never been cleansed since they were built ... The working men's dwellings between Oldfield Road and Cross Lane, where a mass of courts and alleys are to be found in the worst possible state, vie with the dwellings of the Old Town in filth and overcrowding. In this district I found a man, apparently about sixty years old, living in a cow-stable. He had constructed a sort of chimney for his square pen, which had neither windows, floor, nor ceiling, had obtained a bedstead and lived there, though the rain dripped through his rotten roof. This man was too old and weak for regular work, and supported himself by removing manure with a hand-cart; the dung-heaps lay next door to his palace! [5]

Weaste

You went with your father to Weaste, passing the pub nick-named the Widow's Rest as you entered the sullen spacious cemetery through its iron gates. The ground was frozen, wind as harsh as memory as you wandered round. The after-Christmas scene was deadly still. You ambled behind the old bus depot on Eccles New Road and down Mode Wheel Road to the level-crossing near the ship canal.

Strewn across this rigorous landscape were surviving totems of a child's adventuring. Your father was that child. Once upon a time he ran along the high ledge of the cemetery and fell into a pond and didn't drown there, stationed on a muddy island, afraid and calm. He was just another boy – and yet the bearer of the world! Now the area is shrunken, dirtier, altered drastically, if to a plan. Then it was blue and infinite. Now the cemetery calls the tune.

Terraced Ouse Street, where the family lived, was indistinguishable from Europe, as much the epicentre of war as anywhere: bombs were taken, blackouts kept (eclipsing local rivalries), hardship thoroughly was borne. The cobbles in a camber have held out, the last of definition; otherwise the plot is waste. Your father knows the illuminated facet of each stone. How long the short street seemed! and here lived this one, here lived that one, here a Mr Walter Scott, there a Mr Walter Horn, there good Mrs Shepherd. That would have been Mrs Roberts's house, and over there lived Mrs Isabella Egerton. Here Job Lunn the boilermaker lived, and there old Mrs Beckworth who used to hide her pilfered chunks of coal beneath her skirt and always jumped the ration-queue.

Your father in a reverie seems oblivious of your presence. The cloud of phantoms has reality; the past claims him with its agonizing beauty, beautiful because it *is* the past and all of definition.

Into the cemetery a fairground music streams on the wind from the direction of Cross Lane. You visit grandmother's grave, inscribed with her good name. She's just a piece of language at the last, which the wind won't scour away though sharp as any wind in cemeteries. The music is small-town, anachronistic rock 'n' roll. The other graves include Sir Charles Hallé's, which you fail to find, and one Samuel Beckett's.

Greying on the frozen path, your father pads as if in dream but oh so actually alive. You're far away in any case, a traitor-traveller passed on to other places, other kinds of folk, knowing (unkind) a different kind of speech.

You see him from a distance, slight, immeasurable; then he turns. You exit from the graveyard side by side.

Cross Lane (2)

The most obvious thing about the Cross Lane of today is its *absence*. Unlike so much of old Salford which has been eradicated along with all its context and, without a spot of amateur archaeology, can't be discerned clearly enough to be regretted, Cross Lane survives as a glaring emptiness, a broad straight unforgiving thoroughfare virtually denuded of buildings along the way, a tribute to the grim efficiency of modern-day social engineering. For this road was for more than a century one of the liveliest in Salford, a plausible main street in a city that has always been oddly centreless; a road renowned for its cinemas (often former music-halls) – the Palace, the Windsor (or Salford Hippodrome), the Carlton – and inordinate profusion of pubs; the location of an historic cattle market which gave way to a fabled fairground; but now a mere interval of space.

Set back from the pavement are blocks of flats like Albion Towers, the letters of which evocative name are set into the entrance arch of a tube-metal railing adding a queasy touch of painted green to the minutely, drearily mosaicked concrete slabs and prison windows of the tower, whose greyness is that of deadened skies or the colour one might attribute to tears, the tears of utter contingency. On the corner with Broad Street the obelisk commemorating the banker and tireless Christian philanthropist Oliver Heywood, 1825–92, remains *in situ* in the forecourt of an airy and cleanly McDonald's. But in the Corporation, one of four pubs remaining out of scores and which, with the new Salford Religious Centre for Spiritualism at the far end, are the only buildings actually *on* Cross Lane, old Salford in its thick and nasal, *Coronation Street*-ish dialect racily talks on.

Pendleton (1)

Entering 'Salford Shopping City', or 'the precinct' as it's simply called – the one group of low buildings in a horrifically vast estate of high-rises – you immediately feel oppressed. Can you really have been born to this, you ask yourself? Can you get out again quickly, once and for all? The brutal ordinariness, 'common-ness', of the place, the hard penurious faces, the cackle of slangy Salford voices cut you dead. You'd forgotten the accent could be as extreme as *this*! Why can't people phrase things more gracefully? Why can't they dress more tastefully instead of contributing to this garish swirl of synthetic fabrics? Why is there so much 'discounted' rubbish in the shops? Why can't one buy a decent newspaper or cup of coffee? Why must Muzak be continually poured forth, just now Gershwin's *Rhapsody in Blue*?

Ah, Gershwin! the music takes hold of you all the same. Your sympathies relax a little. You start to hear what people are actually saying rather than the mere noise they make. You start to analyse the scene rather than recoiling from it, noticing, for instance, how the old women in their bonnets and dark stockings and sombre woollen coats frequently have faces that are harsh and haggard but sometimes faces that are preternaturally soft and white; or how the strapping young and middle-aged men nearly all sport macho thick moustaches which make them look surprisingly Latin.

Is it much worse, really, than many another city shopping precinct? Isn't it, in fact, distinctly preferable to the vast, yellow-tiled, nauseating development which has long since spread across the centre of Manchester like a disease. (How dismaying to be so thoroughly *Arndaled*!) The Flat Iron outdoor market which is held at one end of the precinct on Mondays, Wednesdays and Saturdays has, you find, a certain vigour, if a certain dinginess. Not just named after the market which was held for centuries around Sacred Trinity church, in a real sense it *is* that market. There's a lot of history here and a healthy appetite for it too: people gather readily at the stall heaped with old prints of the area, commenting on them raucously.

'Respectable' local folk rarely wander round these stalls, still less enter the roomy but vehemently proletarian Flat Iron pub. They prefer to use the precinct on non-market days if use it they must, and they do tend to find the respectable stores like Marks and Spencers and Boots irresistibly convenient. 'Respectable' and 'rough', like 'common' and 'posh', are black and white concepts here in the heart of Pendleton. Holding firm on the side of respectabilty, avoiding any incidences of rough behaviour, being a nice person, are matters of lifelong urgency; for 'roughness' is something that will not go away.

You buy a carton of tea from a refreshments van, walk briskly through the cramped Food Hall and return to the central part of the precinct, glad of the not unattractive sharp-angled glass roofing which helps keep claustrophobia at bay. When people are too much there is always the sky, and today it is even sunny if cold: the Pennines are clearly visible. As you take your leave, albeit impeded by the circuitousness of the walkways and tunnels – it is a precinct favouring motorists – you feel more positive about the place. There is perhaps a hint of the heroic about the widely sweeping architecture, the brave flourish of the *Salford Shopping City* logo and even, somewhere, the planners' social intentions.

Thinking of this sortie when back in London will induce an *after-freshness*.

You have been touched by the precinct unawares.

Bolton Road Playing Fields

Salfordians above the age of twenty-five are habituated to the idea of ruin. Wherever they look they see their familiar buildings corpsed. The roof-beams are showing on the Bolton Road sports pavilion. Only the British Rail name-plate of yellow-bricked Pendleton station isn't a squalid disgrace. The innocent park café is boarded up. Next time they look they find one of those increasingly common vacancies where signification used to be. It is not only that individual buildings – which as often as not is also to say buildings with individuality – are forever disappearing, but whole geographies have been erased from the land-scape, every road and landmark swept away, to exist only in the invisible world of people's memories or the publications of the local history society.

There is much enthusiasm for this society, whose role is not only archival and instructive but no doubt therapeutic. It helps people complete their mourning for the places they have loved. When Irlams o' th' Height was wiped out in the early 1970s, the wound was communal. Where must folks go to recover something of their familiar daily consciousness when the place which gave them their psychological bearings is become just a windy viewing platform, on a good day, for the Pennines? Where but to the local history society?

Nostalgia, one might say, turns pathological. On the other hand, it is the wrong word altogether. A merely sentimental attachment to the old days is more likely to prosper when some evidence of those days remains. This total loss of the past is more like bereavement. One isn't exactly *nostalgic* for departed loved ones.

And yet nothing physical and inanimate is ever really ruined, for *things* are part of an inexorable cycle of making and remaking. The Height cottages so callously bulldozed were slapped down in the first place. The numberless effaced streets of Hanky Park were jerry-built. The blocks of flats that went up and up in their place are no wonders of architectural integrity – they have themselves in many cases now been condemned or razed, even within a decade of construction. Some have been refurbished for university student residences and look marvellously transformed, as by the magic wand of middle-class concern. Whatever comes down can go up again, and be invested with new love. Another Height can be devised. For every vacant lot that appears at dawn like a fairy ring, another gap is plugged, if not always with buildings of peculiarly elaborate character. (But the red and yellow tessellated brickwork distinctive to the area has been adopted at least for the big new bingo hall in the Pendleton precinct.)

There may be a loss of the past's mystery – the big old confidential houses, the cosily tucked-away shops, the secret gardens and surprising vistas – for one person, but for another mystery is conceivably being created. The sprawl of waste land near the Crescent where Christ Church used to be may be an equally alluring object of fantasy for a new generation as Lowry's impressive sooty edifice was for an old. One shouldn't let oneself be bereaved, should one?

Castleway

Ruins are a kind of poetry, in which the beauty of the past flares up with a brightness not otherwise seen, for when the beauty of the past is the beauty of the present, who takes note? It is significant that one of the earliest surviving English poems should be the fragmentary Anglo-Saxon description of a ruin, itself a ruin.

But there is a purely *mental* state of ruin. Back in Salford after months away you are quick to find the area newly tainted, what with reports of muggings in the Irlams o' th' Height area and of an actual, unthinkable shooting on Castleway, most serenely residential of streets; what with a police helicopter chugging deafeningly and calamitously above the house at midnight, and their car-sirens raging in the afternoon; what with a rock group rehearsing when you walk in Oakwood Park and the trees in Light Oaks Park cruelly pollarded, lined up in shame like inmates of a concentration camp. You feel it is all over, the dream of sanctuary, the illusion of the Great Good Place. It was nostalgia and escapism and idealization, but this is the bare reality.

Stepping on to the street to look for that helicopter you ask yourself where, between the balefully whirring blades that seem to slice your dreams and the pointless programmes on the television back indoors, do you stand in the universe now? Abruptly you visualize a line chalked by the police on Castleway around the fallen body and bloodstains on the flagstones.

But the dejection lifts. A glint of sunset gold does much to redeem the lopped trees and reinstate the mystery of the horizons they have long defined. The other park is silent once more, undesecrated, on your next return; while business seems as normal on the Height, and normality doesn't get much more normal than there! The place keeps faith with you after all.

Your worry now is whether you keep faith with it. For do not your endless walks in the parks and relentless meditative designs upon them threaten to bleed these archetypal acres dry of meaning? And wouldn't that be truest ruin, the retrospective annulment of foregone days? Is such a thing possible, you wonder? Can't the spiritual life be mended at least as easily as things of the physical world? Is there no recycling and renewal of an aura?

What *happens* to days? Are they contingent on each other in infinite series? Could it possibly be they radiate from a common centre?

*

Manchester (2)

You had picked up a copy of Mrs Linnaeus Banks's famous novel *The Manchester Man* from an outdoor book table which would once have been located with a host of secondhand stalls on Shude Hill but lies less bohemianly now on Church Street in the Arndale Centre's long shadow; and passed along Dale Street, glancing sidelong at the featureless dark warehouse-canyons of China Lane and Back China Lane; and were strolling up the winding approach to Piccadilly station, the light blue book-jacket plain under your arm, when a stranger touched your elbow, a late middle-aged man with reddish hair, freckles, spectacles, a friendly, quizzical expression and an eager manner of Mancunian speech, exclaiming: 'I noticed the book you were carrying. Have you read it? Are you an admirer of Mrs Banks? I think it's such a *marvellous* book!'

Toc H

No, you could never guess what 'Toc H' meant, and still can't, the conundrum outlasting and memorializing the organization's long demolished meeting-house in Pendleton, hard by the famous half-timbered, long demolished public house at the old turnpike junction, the Woolpack, whose connection with wool was a teaser too; and what was a turnpike? Clearer in your mind was the necessity for a dental clinic to be on a street called Police Street, hard by Pendleton Town Hall, which, however, no longer exist, neither clinic, street nor hall. Place-names need a massier wrecking ball than places.

Pendleton (2)

... the smell of decaying flesh and bones of Blake's bone-yard ... the smell of freshly cut grass at the playing fields further along Duchy Lane ... the smell on passing Asten's pig sties ... the sulphurous smell outside the dyeworks when the boilerman came out with his barrowful of ashes as he declinkered the fires, emptied the material outside and doused the burning pile with water ... the herbal [smell] ... on passing Miller's shop, where they sold homemade dandelion and burdock, sarsaparilla, etc. [The smell] of newsprint in Smith's paper shop next door. [The smell] of chlorine at Mark Fletcher's bleach works near Cock Robin bridge and the musty [smell] of acetylene at Entwistle's sheet metal works nearby.

The boiler works on hot, dry, breezy days issued wisps of red dust from which passers-by experienced the metallic taste of rust ... Nearby at Mandelberg's, the solvent naphtha used in mackintosh manufacture smelled sweet ... Passing the doorway of the works of Eclipse Candy, children would pause to take in deep breaths of the caramel odour of freshly-made toffee ...

The smell of charred wood at Valentine's wheelwright shop when he was fixing a new hot iron hoop on a wooden cartwheel. The smell of paraffin, sold for the variety of bedroom lamps, that pervaded the haberdashery shop of the Misses Wilson of Peter Street, and the tar fumes from the pitch boiler brought in by navvies repairing the cobbled streets, near which children suffering from chest complaints were constrained to stand and sniff . . .[6]

Height Library

Aren't you are becoming a bit eccentric, a bit cracked, incessantly wandering and photographing the streets like this?

The bare sweeping curve of Park Lane (surreal by lamplight), King Street with its weavers' cottages and vanished timber-yard, the charming old Height Library maintaining its useful service after more than ninety years, the old gents' bowling green impassive in the afternoon, and the perfectly ordinary roads, Elleray, Duffield, Alresford, Sumner, Penelope, Hunts – they all have distinct reverberations. Every few yards the area shades into a new specificity of meaning and character, comes under the sway of a new and nameless *genius loci*. There are not, after all, too *many* wards in the city, but too few. Decentralization can't go far enough to recognize a fully human ecology.

Still, people will think you are snooping, a housebreaker on a reconnaissance trip, a council man with powers of compulsory purchase, a rent-collector; or else they'll take you for a malingerer or a wimp, one of those poor backward souls, a bubble at his lips, who never manages to break away from home. And when you use your camera you can be confident of suspicious looks. They don't want you to steal their light, that is true transgression. They worry about what you'll find when the film is printed; perhaps a blow-up will reveal a murder taking place?

'Salford Toccata'

The last thing they assume is that you are in a business of *restoration*; although in their midst, across the road at the end of King Street, his brick walls in the background of your photograph, resides (you happen to know) that great recorder of the local scene, the painter Harold Riley – L.S. Lowry's friend!

Irlams o' th' Height (2)

It was a handloom weaving village then; the click of the shuttle is still in my ear, and in my eye the sight of some stalwart-looking fellows . . . walking away to Manchester with their completed 'cuts' in 'pokes' slung over their shoulders and returning with warp and weft for the next week's work . . . Let me here record that the Irlams o' th' Height folk of that day were, like many other Lancashire weavers, botanists and fond of flowers . . .

The North Mail with its four horses passed every evening along the highway, and l can recollect the sorrow with which I heard that it had run over and killed our watchman, John Henderson. My father has told me how, coming in the dark late from the Bank, he has trotted on his cob, safely behind its shelter.[7]

Hope

You are walking once again along Claremont Road, eyes to the ground – though the morning is fair – noticing pointless things like the rusticated dark-brown coping stones of the garden walls. Buile Hill Park, where early daffodils are out, and Weaste Lane stand bright and peaceful in the sun. Eccles Old Road is not so very busy with traffic. You lift your eyes in the direction of Hope, whose church spire is prominent in the near distance down the hill.

The coping stones on Rivington Road, to your immediate

right, are of the more familiar smooth curved brick, polished by the casual touch of hands over decades. The road is a classically quiet cul-de-sac, short and residential, with roomy, plain and reticent houses, some of whose roofs suggest the conical turret style common to the area. To the left of the road is Hope High School, formerly Hope Hall secondary modern school, formerly Hope Hall private residence, though nothing of that Hope Hall remains (architecturally speaking) in the Hope Halls of yesterday and today. Surviving longer, not eradicated until 10 January 1964, was the stately pile of Chomlea Manor, situated at the end of this cul-de-sac where blocks of flats and little town houses are now. You take a few steps into this estate, remembering the afternoon you spent in one of the flats years ago with a schoolfriend listening to his tape of a rare piece of modern music (you've never seen him since). You wonder how much of the past will signify.

Not much. It is just a dull ordinary scene. You don't see *through* it. One or two idle associations come to mind, but you feel an ennui at being here. You turn away. A second later you are impelled to return for a better look at what you realize are some splendid trees. Four historic poplars in a central reservation seem to burst through the flags. Now the lie of the land slightly adjusts for you, memories deepen, the place takes on the appearance of an historical palimpsest, the burden of its ordinariness decreases. If not exactly on cue, then deflected by the merest elapse of time, the hoped-for signification flows into your consciousness. By a sort of inward emotional calculus you approximate your existential expectations, antipathy turning to love. You have successfully negotiated what, phenomenologically, might be termed eddies of Being.

Walking back along Rivington Road you find that your perspectives on the world have changed. You run a hand along the coping stones. Chomlea Manor is still there, somewhere, and it's not a matter of mere nostalgia. There is a truth of phenomenology beyond all this nostalgia fiddle, you feel. For something like nostalgia was present even in your earliest awe at the great stillnesses – the gardens, rooms and houses – of childhood; an ache then for a Platonic home, perhaps?

The first poem is the poem of ruin. And so it goes.

Portland Street

Your father meets you at Piccadily station on a Saturday night and drives you along Portland Street with its Manchester palazzi, slowing for the traffic through the city's nightclub area, turning right at a crowded Oxford Road, past the disco in the Theatre Royal, past Granada Television with its famous set for *Coronation Street*: the long familiar route to the gentle confine-ment of home. Everything is as it should be, the world seems unthreatening, slightly glowing, and infinitely preordained. But how would these landscapes look if your parents were no longer alive to greet you? What necessity of things would you feel then?

There is a strange, unremarked discontinuity of outlook built into the family, which for the children is always part of the established order of things, an absolute reality, but for the parents is an aspect of contingency, the great *experiment* of their lives!

Buile Hill Park

Tennis players had to wear white. The rule was insisted on in those days. You could never find a rational justification for this, though you searched quite hard for one.

Salford (2)

On a Pendleton market stall a bundle of old picture-postcards sent by Salford folks on holiday. Postmark Blackpool: 'Having a few days at Margery's. The weather continuing good. Love to all. Please excuse scribble, am writing on the bed. Love Mother.' Postmark Torquay: 'Enjoying ourselves here at Torquay. The weather has been pretty good, only one bad day. We have seen quite a lot of Devon and are hoping for more next week. Cheerio for now. Irene and Ken.' Postmark Great Yarmouth: 'Dear Miss Pickering, We are having a nice time on the Norfolk Broads and the weather is good. Hope you are alright. Kind Regards. M. Craig.'

They touch the world and a couple of lives and are gone. Absurd specimens of script preserve them. They *were* doing these things on *those* days.

But it can seem wonderful, when the present is so relentlessly voracious that it devours the best part of a Salford postal district, that anything tangibly survives from the past at all; that there are conduits still – a wisp of tune, a rustle of the wind, the brass touch of a trinket, a sudden bend of lane – opening up unexpectedly to lead us back into what the ethics of nostalgia will occasionally permit us to call a better world. And Salfordians hug their photograph albums. They enjoy the game of mentally rebuilding their vanished townscapes as though pulling the flaps of a toy theatre; and sometimes they commit their memories to print. The local history society publishes books of such recollections, which tend to be eloquent and touching, and if not quite art, embody the eternal impulse of art. You are always struck by the acute difference of effect when a writer's memories overlap with your own.

People cling all the more obsessively to old photographs

when their loss is not just time past – the common lot – but great tracts of community space. Internal landscapes fade reliably if benignly, and photographs of even the best known scene can induce a shock of recognition positively sensual. You see those fascinating little corners and dark recesses once more, you have let slip even the *idea* of them; but there they are again in all their enticing obduracy of existence. The touch of time is, as the poet suggested, 'unimaginable'. The touch of the camera's lens upon the vanished light of these realities – most ineffably gentle of 'Salford toccatas' – is, though, precisely imaginable.

And yet you are baulked one morning back in London by the receipt of a collection of such photos in which the past lives truthfully enough – you descry a window-cleaner about to cross the Height with bucket and squelchy leather, it's the man himself – but the reproduction is too dark and, contrary to mythology, you find that the sun is not always shining on the summers of childhood. You don't know how to get round this, how to turn the image and yourself to the light. You would almost rather not have the photos if you can't see properly what's there, what *was* there. There is no give here. There is only this vaguely helpful but dumb document, this thing in your life again called 'Salford', this beautiful but vaguely ruinous idea – *the past.*

References

1. *Salford – A City and its Past*, ed. Tom Bergin, et al., City of Salford, 1989.
2. Thomas De Quincey, *Confessions of an English Opium-Eater* (1856), Masson edn, footnote to volume 3, page 237.
3. L.S. Lowry quoted in Allen Andrews, *The Life of L.S. Lowry*, Jupiter Books, 1977.

4. Daniel Defoe, Letter 10, *A Tour Through the Whole Island of Great Britain, 1724–6*, Penguin, 1971.
5. Friedrich Engels, *The Condition of the Working Class in England*, Penguin, 1987.
6. Ike Chapman, *Brindleheath, A Salford Village*, Neil Richardson, 1981.
7. Oliver Heywood, letter to the editor, St John's parish magazine, 18 December 1886, quoted in Barbara Watson, *Irlams o' th' Height – The Growth and Destruction of a Village 1600–1987*, Neil Richardson, 1987.

Acknowledgements

For their particular kindnesses and advice I would like to thank Robin and Boo Chapman, Neil Corcoran, Nicholas Everett, Paul Keegan, Michael Kennedy, Ian McQueen, Margo Miller, Hilda Morley, Bayan Northcott, Alexandra Pringle, Jon Riley, Miranda Seymour, Jo Shapcott, Geoffrey Wall and Joanna Weinberger.

I owe special debts to Asa Brigg's *Victorian Cities* (Penguin, 1963), Michael Kennedy's *Portrait of Manchester* (Robert Hale, 1970), Alan Kidd's *Manchester* (Ryburn, 1993), Tilly Marshall's *Life with Lowry* (Hutchinson, 1981), Shelley Rohde's *A Private View of L.S. Lowry* (Collins, 1979) and V.I. Tomlinson's *Salford in Pictures* (E.J. Morten, 1974).

I am grateful to the John Rylands University Library of Manchester, most beautiful of working-places.

The nanswer to the implied riddle of 'Two Poems' is Beethoven.

*

The author and publishers greatfully acknowledge permission to publish the following.

The translation of lines by Rainer Maria Rilke on page 161 is taken from Volume 2, Poetry, of the *Selected Works of Rilke*, translated by J.B. Leishman, published by Chatto & Windus in 1960.